100 YEARS OF POPULAR

80s - Volume 1

Series Editor:
Carol Cuellar

Editorial and Production:
Artemis Music Limited

Design and Production:
JPCreativeGroup.com

Published 2003

International Music Publications Limited
Griffin House 161 Hammersmith Road London W6 8BS England

IMP

International
Music
Publications

CONTENTS

TITLE	PAGE
ALL I SEE IS YOU	12
BOBBY'S GIRL	9
CABARET	16
CAN'T HELP FALLING IN LOVE	20
THE CAPTAIN OF YOUR SHIP	23
THE CARNIVAL IS OVER	26
COME OUTSIDE	29
CONGRATULATIONS	38
DELILAH	34
DIDN'T WE	43
EVERYBODY'S TALKIN'	46
FINGS AIN'T WOT THEY USED T'BE	49
GENTLE ON MY MIND	52
GEORGY GIRL	56
THE GOOD LIFE	59
GREEN GREEN GRASS OF HOME	62
A GROOVY KIND OF LOVE	66
HALFWAY TO PARADISE	74
HAPPY BIRTHDAY SWEET SIXTEEN	69
HAPPY HEART	78
HELLO DOLLY	81
HONEY	86
I CAN'T STOP LOVING YOU	91
I CLOSE MY EYES AND COUNT TO TEN	94
I ONLY WANT TO BE WITH YOU	98
I PRETEND	102
I'M COMING HOME	105
I'M TELLING YOU NOW	108
IF EVER I WOULD LEAVE YOU	110
IF I RULED THE WORLD	120
IF I WERE A CARPENTER	126
THE IMPOSSIBLE DREAM	115
IT MIGHT AS WELL RAIN UNTIL SEPTEMBER	130
IT MUST BE HIM	133
JUST LOVING YOU	136
LAST WALTZ	142

TITLE	PAGE

LES BICYCLETTES DE BELSIZE 139

LITTLE CHILDREN 146

LITTLE GREEN APPLES 150

THE LOCO-MOTION 156

MASSACHUSETTS 162

MAY EACH DAY 164

MILORD 170

MY CHERIE AMOUR 159

MY KIND OF GIRL 174

MY WAY 178

ON A CLEAR DAY (YOU CAN SEE FOREVER) 182

PORTRAIT OF MY LOVE 186

PUPPET ON A STRING 188

SAY WONDERFUL THINGS 192

SILENCE IS GOLDEN 198

SOFTLY, AS I LEAVE YOU 195

SPANISH EYES (MOON OVER NAPLES) 200

STRANGER ON THE SHORE 202

TAKE THESE CHAINS FROM MY HEART 205

THERE GOES MY EVERYTHING 208

THERE'S A KIND OF HUSH
  (ALL OVER THE WORLD) 211

TRY TO REMEMBER 214

UP ON THE ROOF 217

UP UP AND AWAY 220

WALK AWAY 224

THE WEDDING 228

WHAT A WONDERFUL WORLD 232

THE WHITE ROSE OF ATHENS 238

A WHITER SHADE OF PALE 240

WINCHESTER CATHEDRAL 235

WORDS 242

A WORLD OF OUR OWN 246

YOU DON'T HAVE TO SAY YOU LOVE ME 250

YOU'RE MY WORLD (IL MIO MONDO) 256

60s

Revolutionary... if we could pick only one word to describe the '60s, this would be it. During these ten turbulent years, many of our preconceived notions about ourselves, and our society, were suddenly turned upside down. They have never been the same since.

The birth control pill sparked a "sexual revolution". Women's skirts kept getting shorter, while men's hair grew ever longer. From Cornwall to Dover, and London to Leeds, young people were dropping out and tuning in, questioning old precepts and looking for new meaning. Conformity would no longer do; the new generation had set out on a voyage of self-discovery, intent not only on transforming themselves, but the world itself.

Meanwhile, technology moved ahead at a breathtaking pace. Doctors performed the first human heart transplants and began implanting artificial hearts in patients. Early photocopying machines and computers began to change the

office workplace. People had not only travelled into outer space, by the end of the decade we had actually walked on the moon.

Technology was also changing the world of music. Robert Moog invented the "Moog synthesizer", ushering in the era of electronic music. The monaural recordings of earlier decades had given way to stereo, and FM had replaced AM as the primary radio band.

Much of the best music of the era drew an almost mystical sort of energy from the swirl of events that made up the '60s experience. A good example is the progressive rock opus "A Whiter Shade Of Pale" from Procol Harum. Starting out as an R&B group in Essex, this band went through a series of personnel changes in the '60s, as it ventured deeper and deeper into unknown musical territory.

By 1967, Procol Harum and its distinctive sound had clearly come of age. The group first performed "A Whiter Shade Of Pale" in May at the Speakeasy Club in London. On June 4, Procol Harum opened for Jimi Hendrix at the Saville Theatre. Less than one week later, "A Whiter Shade Of Pale" reached the top of the UK charts and was on its way to becoming one of the best-selling progressive rock songs of all time.

Blending Bach-inspired keyboard interludes with surreal lyrics, "A Whiter Shade Of Pale" transported listeners to a different reality level. Gary Brooker's haunting vocals and Matthew Fisher's ethereal organ only added to the mystical effect.

Always in a state of flux, Procol Harum began to dissolve just as "A Whiter Shade Of Pale" was peaking. Some members of the group left, to be replaced by new musicians. Although the reformed band would continue to record great music and enjoy commercial success, the original group behind one of the '60s' most evocative songs had been as fleeting as the smoke of burning incense.

Happy Songs

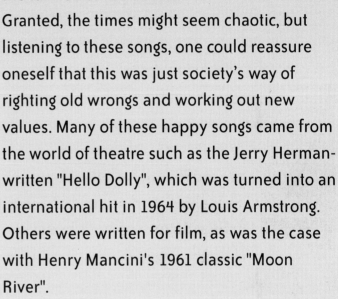

In contrast to "A Whiter Shade Of Pale," other songs of the '60s offered a welcome break from the turmoil of the decade. Granted, the times might seem chaotic, but listening to these songs, one could reassure oneself that this was just society's way of righting old wrongs and working out new values. Many of these happy songs came from the world of theatre such as the Jerry Herman-written "Hello Dolly", which was turned into an international hit in 1964 by Louis Armstrong. Others were written for film, as was the case with Henry Mancini's 1961 classic "Moon River".

"Georgy Girl" by the Australian folk-rock group The Seekers was another breezy feel-good song from the movies. Yet this simple tune, which was the title song to the 1966 Lynn Redgrave/James Mason film, also had a deeper meaning, more in tune with the spirit of the times. In the song, as well as the movie, the main character is encouraged to find herself and express her deepest desires, so that the world might see "a new Georgy Girl".

Tom Jones treated fans to a steady stream of exuberant good-time hits during the '60s. The Welsh-born singer with the rich, full-

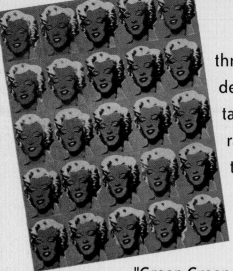

throated baritone demonstrated his talents on a wide range of songs, from the dark and sensuous "Delilah", to the touching country song "Green Green Grass Of Home".

Rock and roll had clearly established itself as the dominant form of popular music by the early '60s. Perhaps this gave rock artists the confidence to relax and inject an element of humour into their work. For whatever reason, the '60s witnessed an explosion of "spoof" songs that served up great music with a lighthearted twist.

Among the most popular of these songs was "Winchester Cathedral" by the New Vaudeville Band. Producer and composer Geoff Stephens wrote this spoof song and recorded it with an anonymous group of musicians. John Carter, who was responsible for the vocals, sang through his hands to simulate the sound of a megaphone.

In 1966, during the middle of the "revolutionary '60", this lighthearted parody about lost love reached music fans everywhere. "Winchester Cathedral" became a Top Five hit in England. It did even better in America, where it reached the No.1 position and won a Grammy Award.

The Manchester group Herman's Hermits brought a lighthearted and airy touch to new rock and classic music hall songs during the '60s to attract a large fan following in the UK and the US. Originally called The Heartbeats, the group, which was led by the teenage Peter Noone, had 16 Top 20 singles in Britain and America between 1964 and 1970. During one 12-month period, they sold an impressive 10 million records. Their cover of the Sam Cooke classic "What A Wonderful World" reached No. 4 on the US Charts, as did their sweetly romantic ballad "There's A Kind Of Hush". This song peaked at No.7 on the UK charts.

Girls Rule

With few exceptions, female artists stayed in the shadows during the early years of rock and roll, typically performing as background singers or part of a male-dominated group. This all began to change in the '60s, the decade that spawned the modern "women's lib" movement.

Almost from the beginning of the decade, the '60s brought us a new generation of female stars. Bold and confident, these young artists were unapologetic in addressing issues from a woman's perspective in their music. The style and substance of their songs enriched rock and roll, making it more complete.

Among the most celebrated and influential new female stars of the '60s was London-born Mary Isabel Catherine Bernadette O'Brien – or, as she would become known throughout the world, Dusty Springfield. During the early 1960s, when the British pop scene was dominated by the Mersey Beat sound, Springfield took a daring step by leaving her successful pop/folk group The Springfields to embark on a solo career as an R&B-oriented artist.

In late 1963, Springfield had her first solo hit, the triumphantly passionate "I Only Want To Be With You". Highlighting Springfield's sprightly rhythm and warm voice, the song became a smash hit, reaching the Top Five in the UK and coming close to cracking the American Top 10 in 1964. Interestingly, this was the first major US hit by an artist from the UK since The Beatles launched the famous "British invasion" of the American music scene. "I Only

Want To Be With You" was also the first song ever performed on the long-running television programme *Top Of The Pops*.

Springfield followed this song with a series of other hits like "All I See Is You" and the 1966 international hit "You Don't Have To Say You Love Me". This powerful song of conflicting emotions and raw vulnerabilities reached the top of the charts in the UK and the Top Five in the US. It was translated for Springfield from the Italian song "Io Che Non Vivo (Senzate)".

Perhaps more than any other figure of the '60s, this sweet, but iron-willed, woman with the distinctive blond beehive and dark "panda bear" eye makeup was responsible for popularising the African-American-style soul music in Britain. In 1965, while at the height of her fame, she hosted the television program *Soul Of Motown*, throwing a well-deserved spotlight on this musical genre.

Springfield's commitment to bridging the racial divide extended beyond music to other areas of life. In 1964, the apartheid government of South Africa deported her from the country, after she refused to perform at venues where the crowd was racially segregated.

The great singer Dionne Warwick was one of the many artists whose career in Britain was helped by the attention Springfield drew to African-American music. In 1964, the former gospel singer from New Jersey made her debut

on the UK charts with "Anyone Who Had A Heart". Written by the famous team of Burt Bacharach and Hal David, this song was also a hit for Dusty Springfield. Warwick's perfect phrasing and sophisticated treatment of R&B themes made songs like "Walk On By" hugely popular with black and white audiences alike.

No true fan of '60s cinema will ever forget Cilla Black's evocative recording of the theme song from *Alfie*, the film that transformed Michael Caine into an international superstar. Her plaintive refrain, "What's it all about Alfie?" not only captured the underlying message of this movie set in London of the swinging '60s, but also spoke of the search for new inner personal meaning that preoccupied so many young people of the era.

As it had throughout history, music served two very different purposes in the '60s. It offered people a chance to express their deepest and most disquieting feelings, while at the same time providing them with a means of escaping into pure flights of harmonic fantasy. So savour this '60s musical sampler. We think you'll agree that in addition to tie-dye shirts and lava lamps, this momentous decade produced some of the most memorable songs of all time.

Ten Things That First Appeared In The '60s

1. Men on the moon.

2. Love beads.

3. Office cubicle.

4. Freeze-dried coffee.

5. Hand-held calculators.

6. Laser eye surgery.

7. Touch-tone phones.

8. Compact audio cassette tapes.

9. Computer mouse.

10. Soft fibre-tipped pens.

BOBBY'S GIRL

Words and Music by HENRY HOFFMAN and GARY KLEIN

ALL I SEE IS YOU

Words and Music by CLIVE WESTLAKE and BEN WEISMAN

14

CABARET

Words by FRED EBB
Music by JOHN KANDER

1. What good is sit-ting a-lone in your room?___
2. Put down the knit-ting, the book and the broom,___

Come hear the mu-sic play.___
time for a ho-li-day.___

CAN'T HELP FALLING IN LOVE

Words and Music by GEORGE WEISS,
HUGH PERETTI, and LUIGI CREATORE

21

22

THE CAPTAIN OF YOUR SHIP

Words and Music by KENNY YOUNG and BEN YARDLEY

1. This is the cap - tain of___ your ship,___ your heart speak - in' we've run in - to___ a lit - tle storm,___ the
2. This is the cap - tain of___ your ship,___ your soul call - in', you'd bet - ter turn___ your - self___ a - round,___ there's

THE CARNIVAL IS OVER

Words and Music by TOM SPRINGFIELD

28

COME OUTSIDE

Words and Music by CHARLES BLACKWELL

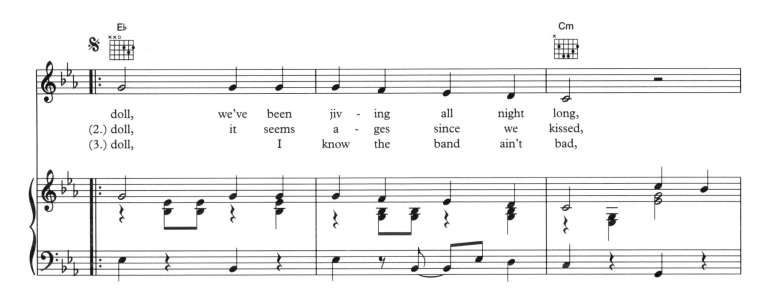

DELILAH

Words and Music by LES REED and BARRY MASON

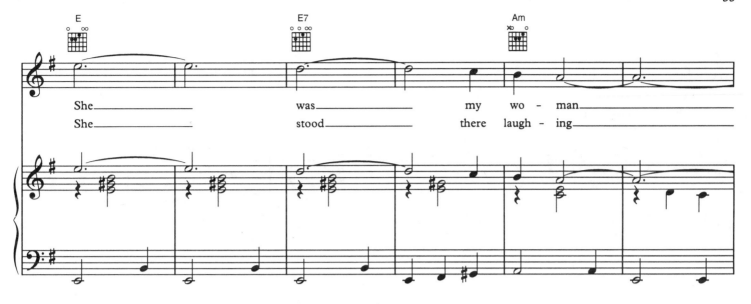

She_____ was_____ my wo - man_____
She_____ stood_____ there laugh - ing_____

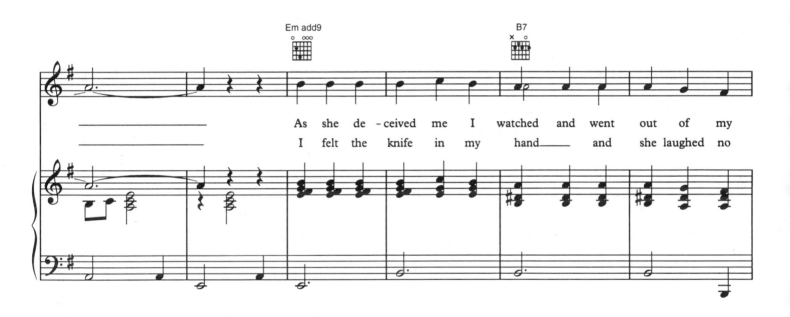

_____ As she de - ceived me I watched and went out of my
_____ I felt the knife in my hand_____ and she laughed no

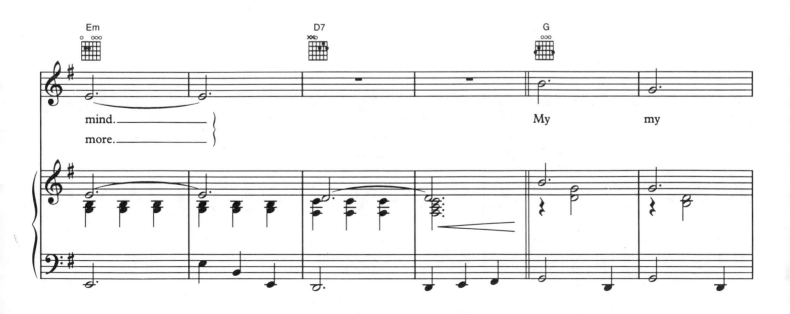

mind._____ My my
more._____

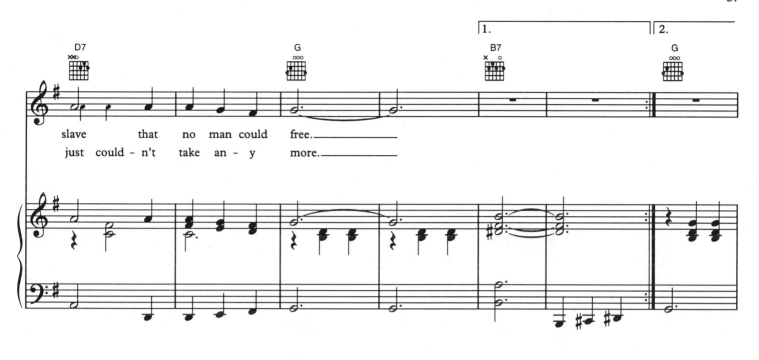

slave that no man could free.————————
just could-n't take an-y more.————————

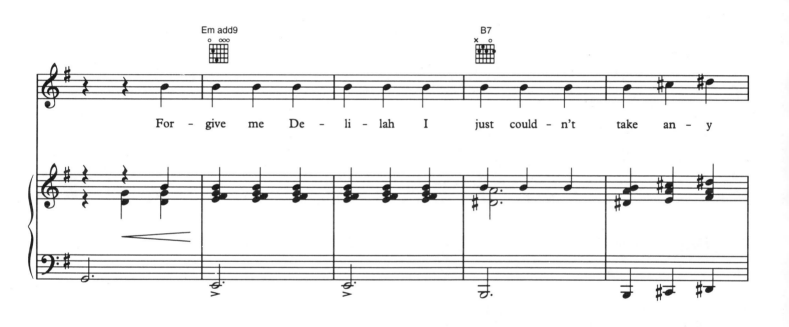

For - give me De - li - lah I just could - n't take an - y

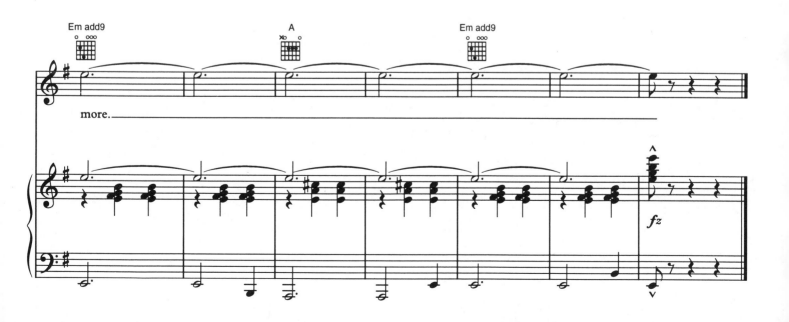

more.————————————————————————————

CONGRATULATIONS

Words and Music by BILL MARTIN and PHIL COULTER

Medium Tempo

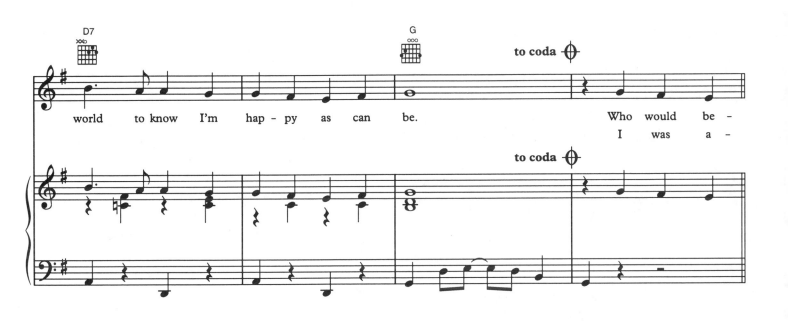

think that hap – pi – ness had – n't been in – vent – ed   but that was
on – ly fool – ing my – self to think you'd love   me   but then to –

in   the bad old   days   be – fore I   met   you_____
night you said you   could – n't live with – out   me_____

—   when I let you_____ walk in – to my   heart._____
—   that round a – bout me_____ you want – ed to   stay._____

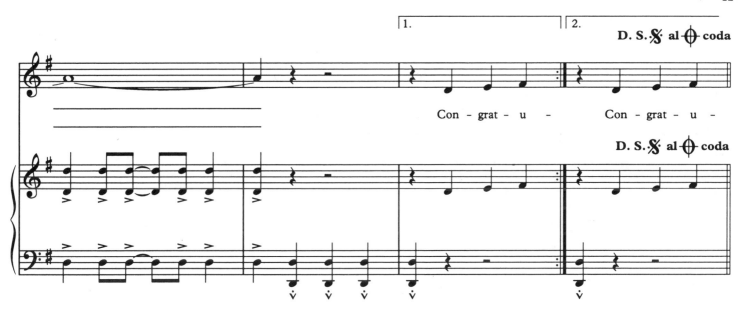

Coda

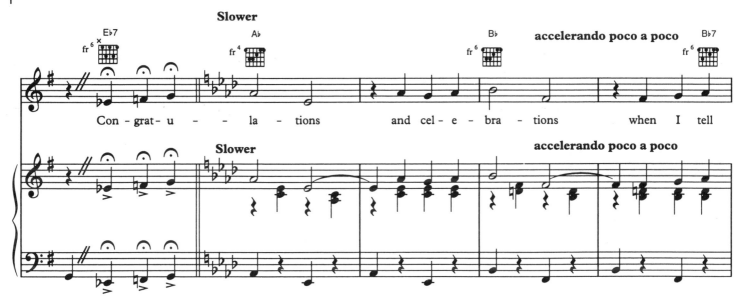

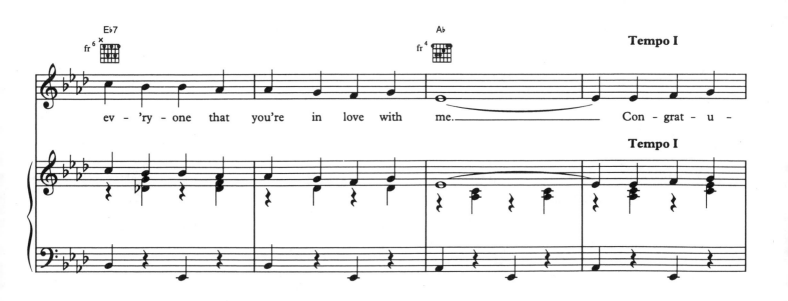

DIDN'T WE

Words and Music by JIM WEBB

EVERYBODY'S TALKIN'

Words and Music by FRED NEIL

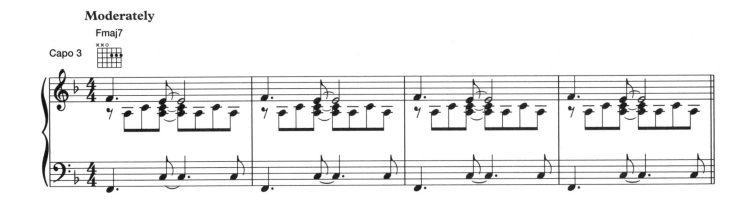

Ev-ery-bo-dy's talk-in' at __ me, I don't hear a word they're say - in',

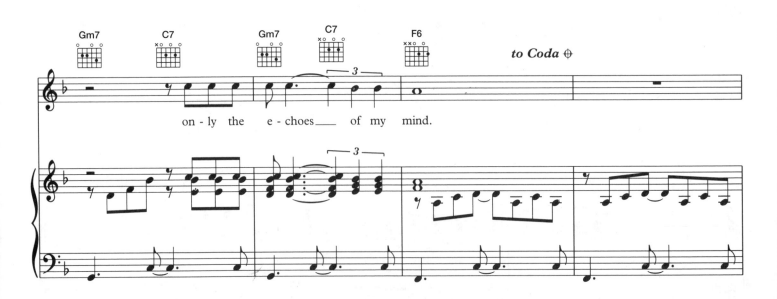

on-ly the e-choes__ of my mind.

FINGS AIN'T WOT THEY USED T' BE

Words and Music by LIONEL BART

do- -ing knees up rock— 'n' roll,
side our doors to greet— us, No,
I've got news from El - vis P,
} Fings ain't wot they used t'

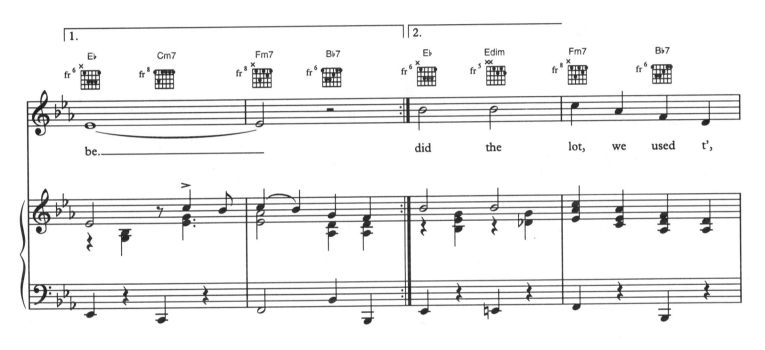

1.
be._____

2.
did the lot, we used t',

fings ain't wot they used t' be._____

GENTLE ON MY MIND

Words and Music by JOHN HARTFORD

54

2. It's not mind.

3. Though the wheat-fields and the clothes lines and the junk-yards and the highways come between us
And some other woman crying to her mother 'cause she turned and I was gone
I still might run in silence, tears of joy might stain my face
And a summer sun might burn me 'til I'm blind
But not to where I cannot see you walkin' on the back-roads
By the rivers flowing gentle on my mind.

4. I dip my cup of soup back from the gurglin' cracklin' cauldron in some train yard
My beard a roughning coal pile and a dirty hat pulled low across my face
Through cupped hands 'round a tin can I pretend
I hold you to my breast and find
That you're waving from the back-roads by the rivers of my mem'ry
Ever smilin', ever gentle on my mind.

GEORGY GIRL

Words by JIM DALE
Music by TOM SPRINGFIELD

Baion tempo (not fast)

Hey there! Geor-gy girl___ swing-ing down the street so fan-cy free,

no-bod-y you meet could ev-er see the lone-li-ness there in-side you.

Hey there! Geor-gy girl___

why do all the boys just pass you by?

dream-ing of the some-one you could be.

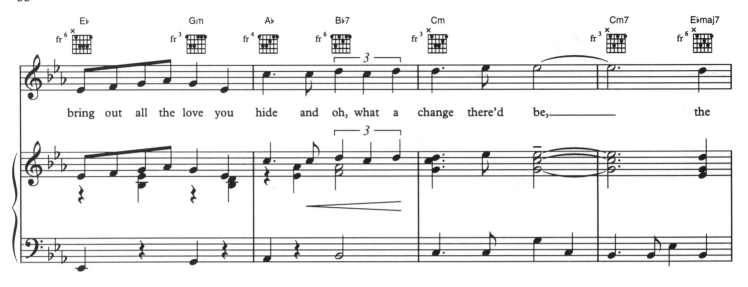

bring out all the love you hide and oh, what a change there'd be,_____ the

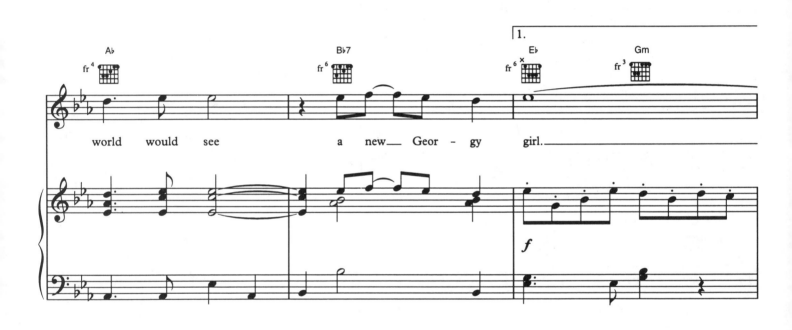

world would see a new__ Geor - gy girl._____

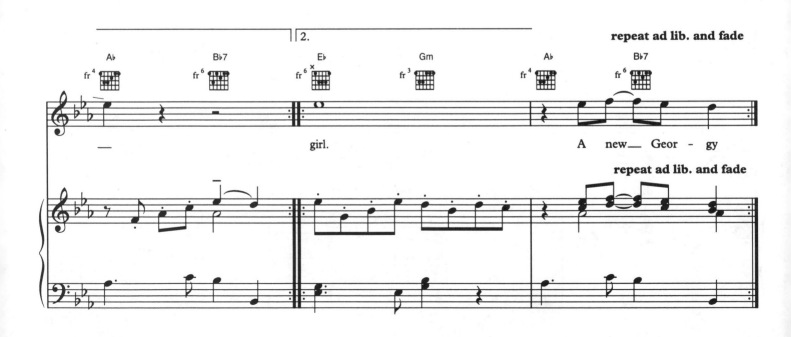

__ girl. A new__ Geor - gy

repeat ad lib. and fade

THE GOOD LIFE

Words by JACK REARDON
Music by SACHA DISTEL

Slowly (with feeling)

Oh, the good life_____ full of fun_____ seems to be_____ the i-deal,

yes, the good life_____ lets you hide_____ all the sad - ness you feel._____ You won't

Please re-mem-ber_____ I still want you_____ and in case you_____ won-der why,_____ well, just wake up_____ kiss the good life_____ good- bye._____ Oh, the bye._____

GREEN GREEN GRASS OF HOME

Words and Music by CURLY PUTMAN

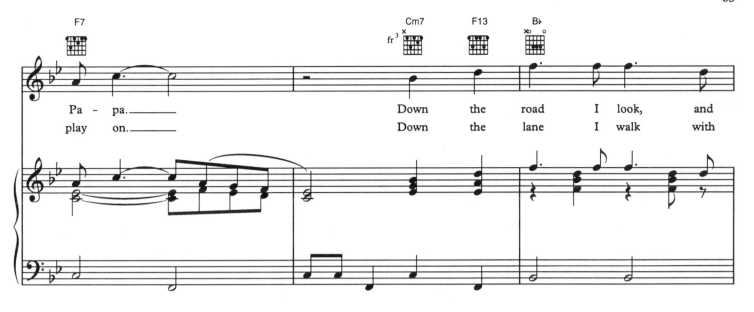

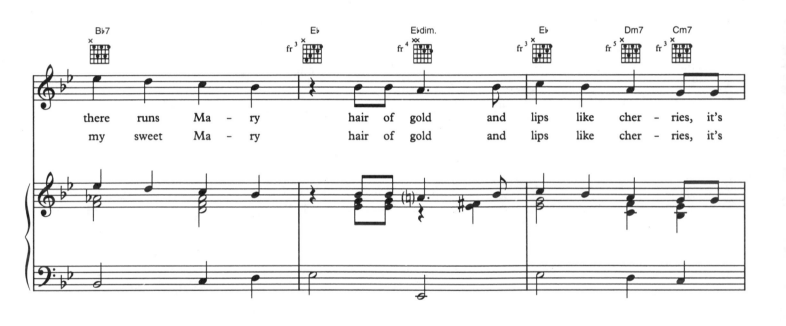

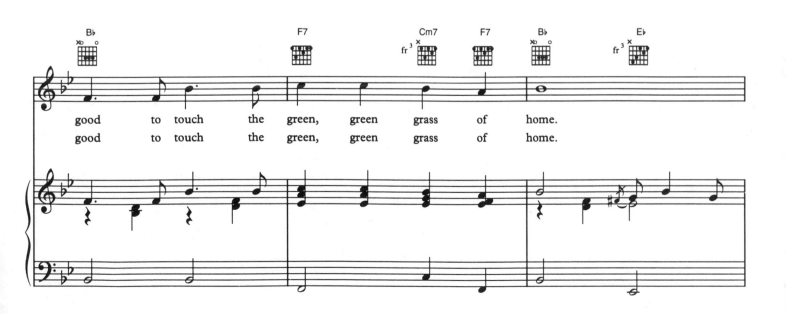

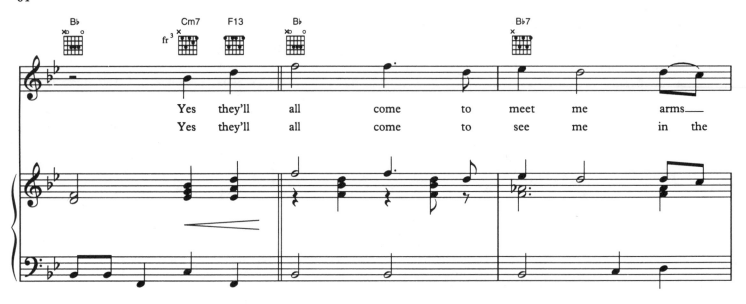

Yes they'll all come to meet me arms___
Yes they'll all come to see me in the

1. 2.

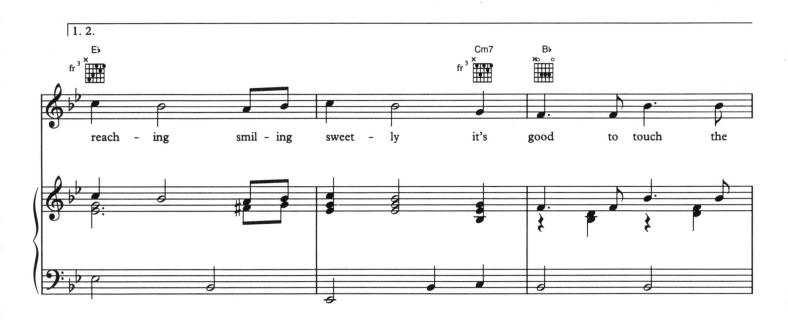

reach - ing smil - ing sweet - ly it's good to touch the

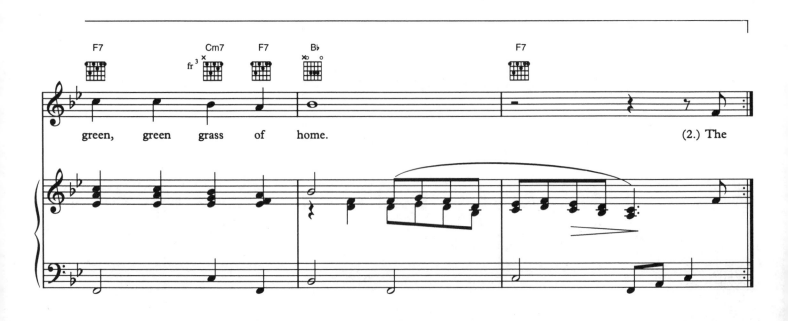

green, green grass of home. (2.) The

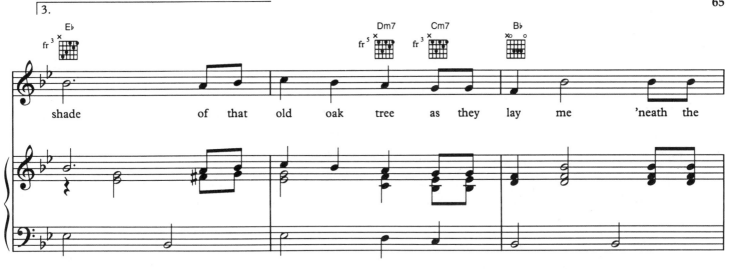

shade of that old oak tree as they lay me 'neath the

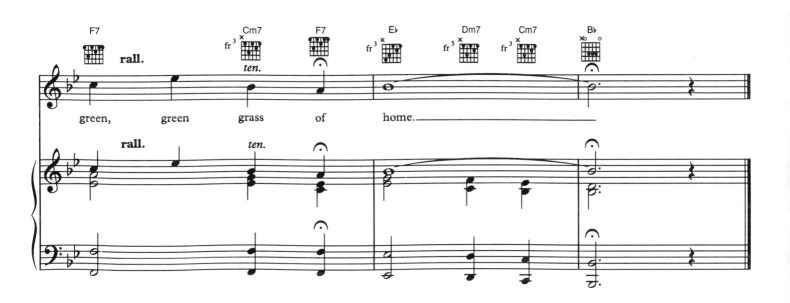

green, green grass of home.

VERSE 3. (spoken) Then I awake and look around me
at four grey walls that surround me,
And I realize that I was only dreaming,
For there's a guard and there's a sad old padre
- arm in arm we'll walk at daybreak
Again I'll touch the green, green grass of home.

A GROOVY KIND OF LOVE

Words and Music by TONI WINE and CAROLE BAYER SAGER

HAPPY BIRTHDAY SWEET SIXTEEN

Words and Music by NEIL SEDAKA and HOWARD GREENFIELD

73

HALFWAY TO PARADISE

Words and Music by GERRY GOFFIN and CAROLE KING

HAPPY HEART

Words by JACKIE RAE
Music by JAMES LAST

HELLO DOLLY

Words and Music by JERRY HERMAN

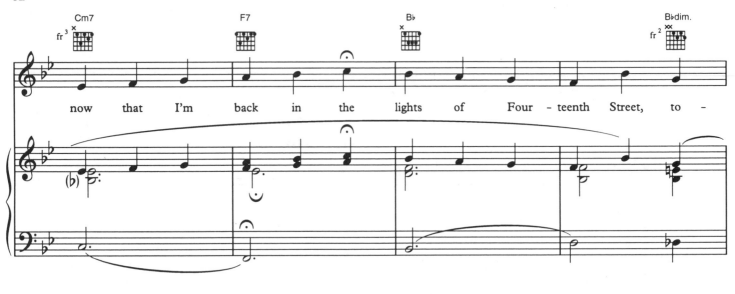

now that I'm back in the lights of Four-teen Street, to-

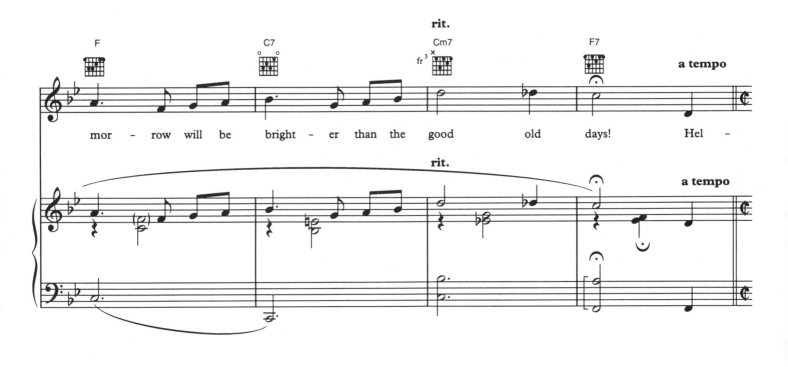

mor-row will be bright-er than the good old days! Hel-

lo, Dol-ly, well, hel-lo, Dol-ly, it's so

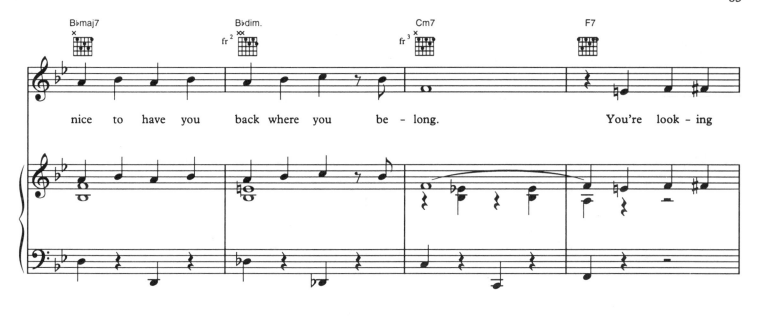

nice to have you back where you be - long. You're look - ing

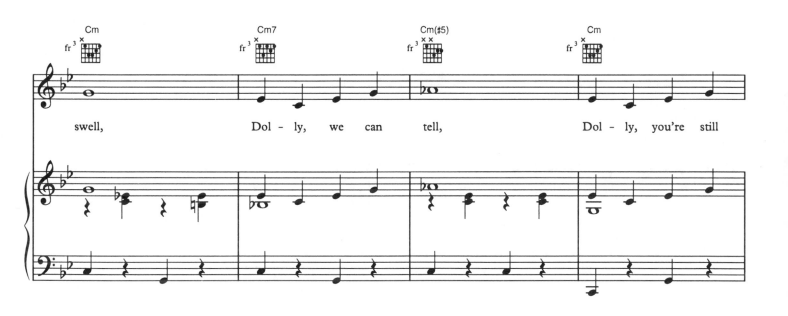

swell, Dol - ly, we can tell, Dol - ly, you're still

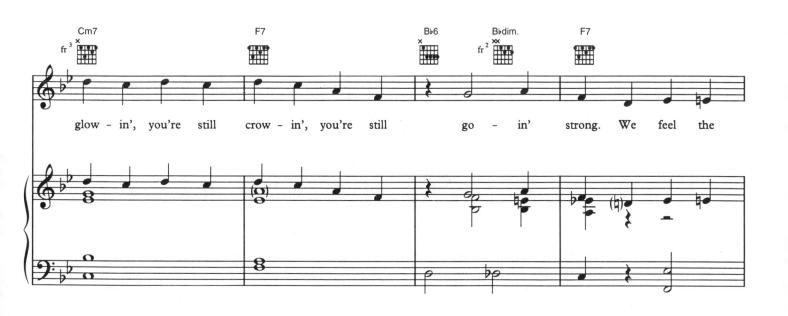

glow - in', you're still crow - in', you're still go - in' strong. We feel the

room _____ sway - in', for the band's _____ play - in' one of

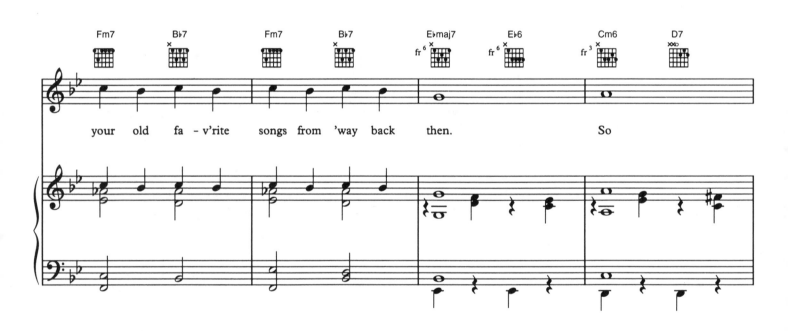

your old fa - v'rite songs from 'way back then. _____ So

take her wrap, fel - las, find her an emp - ty lap, fel - las,
gol - ly gee, fel - las, find her a va - cant knee, fel - las,

HONEY

Words and Music by BOBBY RUSSELL

See the tree, how big it's grown, but friend it has-n't been too long, it
Then the first snow came and she ran out to brush the snow a - way so it

was - n't big.   I laughed at her and she got mad, the
would - n't die.   Came run - 'nin in_____ all ex - cit - ed

I CAN'T STOP LOVING YOU

Words and Music by DON GIBSON

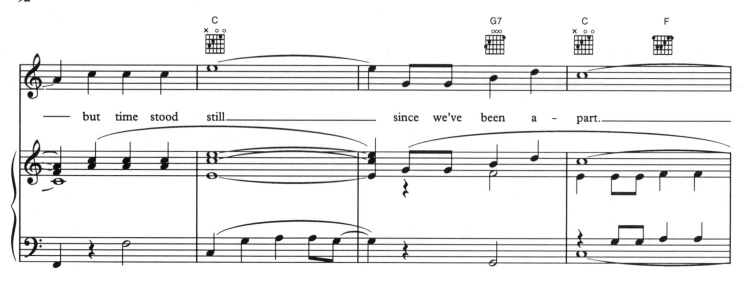

but time stood still_____ since we've been a - part._____

— I can't stop lov - ing you,_____ I've made up my mind_____ to live in

mem - o - ry_____ of old lone - some times._____ I can't stop

I CLOSE MY EYES AND COUNT TO TEN

Words and Music by CLIVE WESTLAKE

I ONLY WANT TO BE WITH YOU

Words and Music by MIKE HAWKER and IVOR RAYMONDE

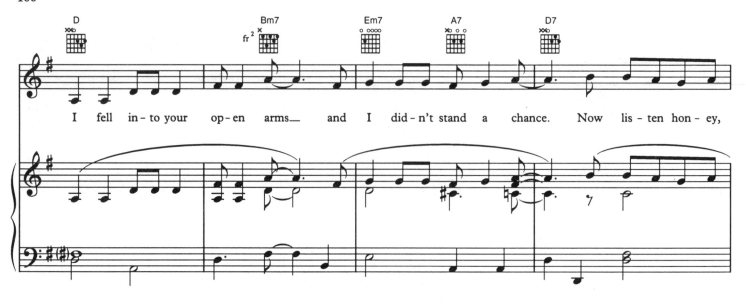

I fell in-to your op-en arms__ and I did-n't stand a chance. Now lis-ten hon-ey,

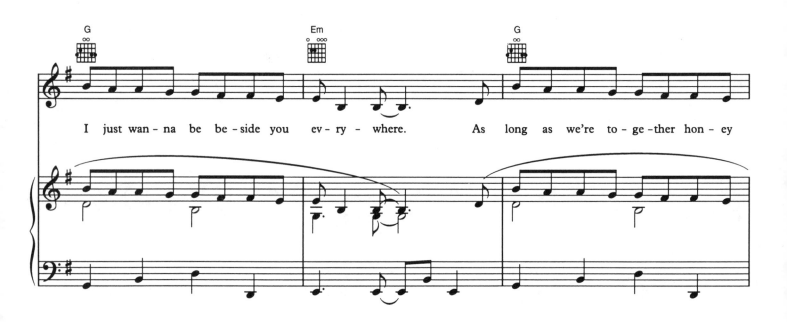

I just wan-na be be-side you ev-ry-where. As long as we're to-ge-ther hon-ey

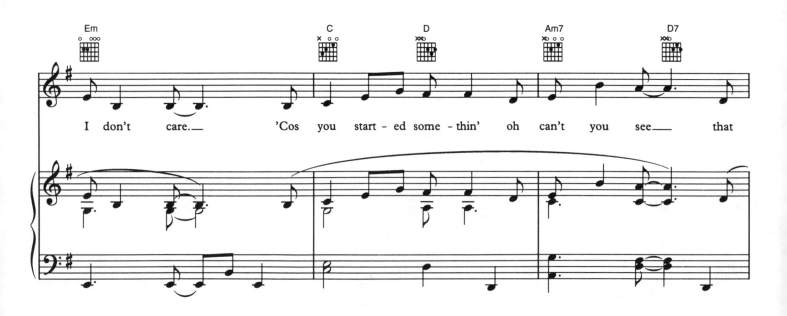

I don't care.__ 'Cos you start-ed some-thin' oh can't you see__ that

I PRETEND

Words and Music by LES REED and BARRY MASON

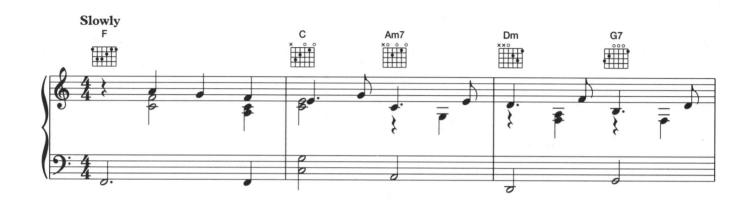

1. Sit-ting here so lone-ly in the fire-light,
2. Some-thing made her change, what could it be now?

listen-ing for a foot-step on the stair. All I have to talk to is the
Wish I knew ex-act-ly what I'd done. If there's some-one else, I'll set you

I'M COMING HOME

Words and Music by LES REED and BARRY MASON

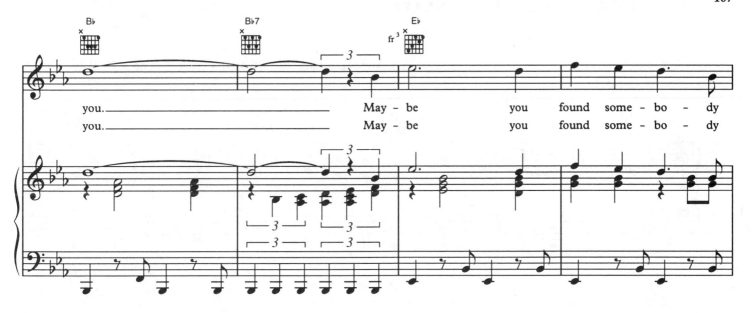

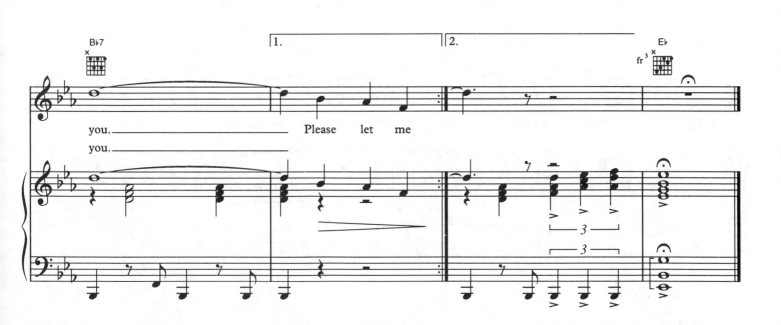

I'M TELLING YOU NOW

Words and Music by FREDDIE GARRITY and MITCH MURRAY

IF EVER I WOULD LEAVE YOU

Words by ALAN JAY LERNER
Music by FREDERICK LOEWE

I've seen how you spar - kle_____ when fall nips the air._____

_____ I know you in au - tumn_____ and I must be there.

And could I leave you run - ning mer - ri - ly through the snow?_____

Or on a win-try eve-ning when you catch the fi-re's glow?

If ev-er I would leave you,_____ how could it be in spring-time,_____

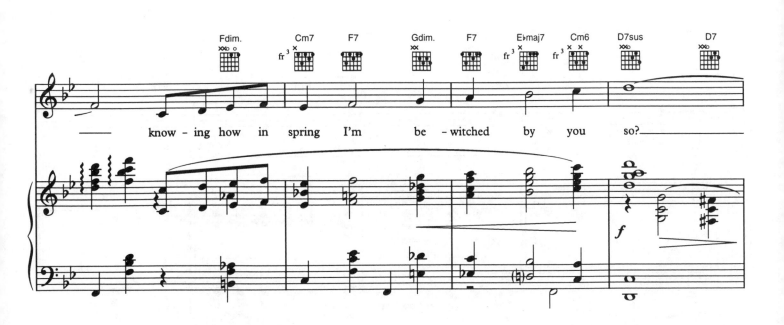

_____ know-ing how in spring I'm be-witched by you so?_____

THE IMPOSSIBLE DREAM

Words by JOE DARSON
Music by MITCH LEIGH

bear_____ with un‑bear‑a‑ble sor‑row,_____ to

try_____ when your arms are too wea‑ry,_____ to

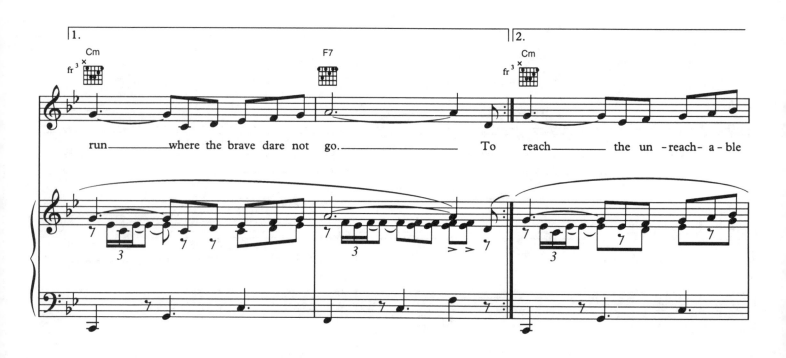

run_____ where the brave dare not go._____ To reach_____ the un‑reach‑a‑ble

star! This is my quest,_____ to fol‑low that

118

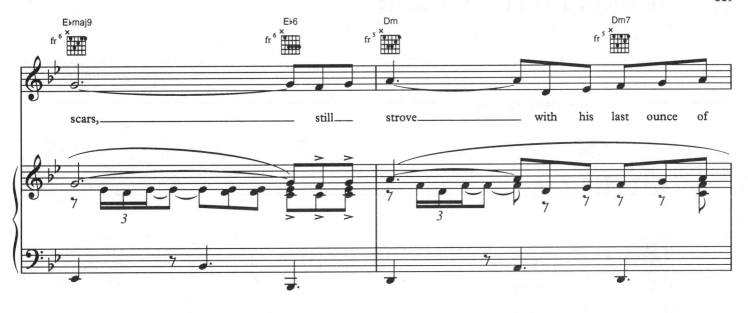

IF I RULED THE WORLD

Words by LESLIE BRICUSSE
Music by CYRIL ORNADEL

Steady moderate tempo

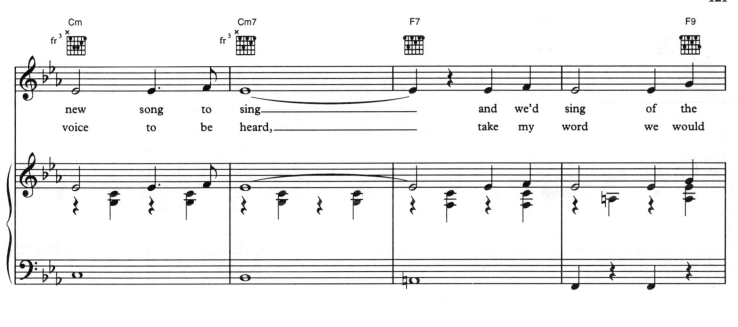

new song to sing_____ and we'd sing of the
voice to be heard,_____ take my word we would

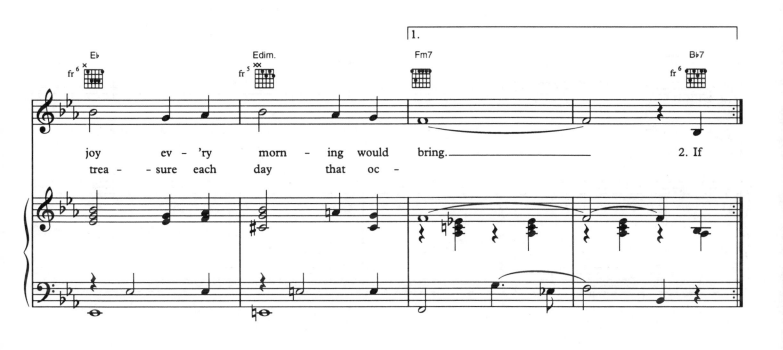

1.
joy ev-'ry morn-ing would bring._____ 2. If
trea--sure each day that oc-

2.
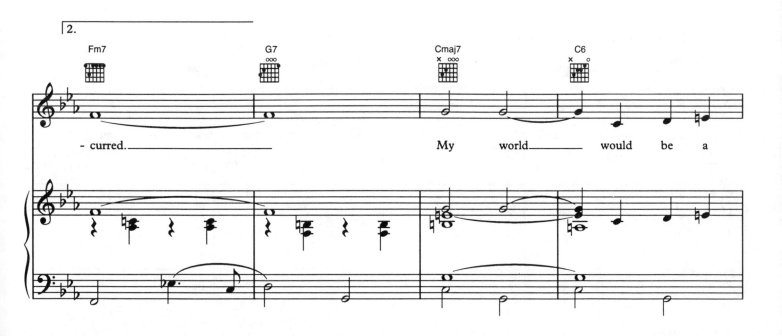

-curred._____ My world_____ would be a

beau – ti – ful place,____ where we would weave such won – der – ful

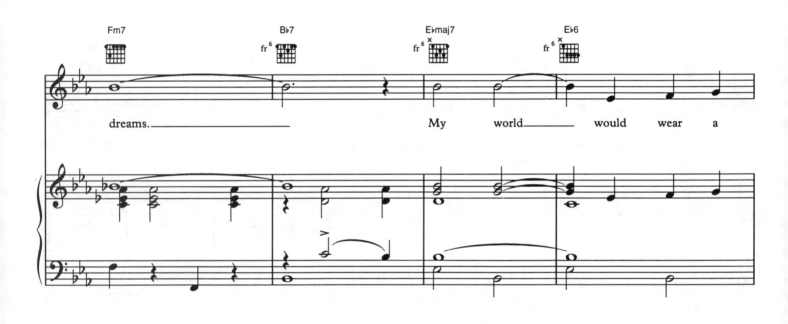

dreams._____ My world____ would wear a

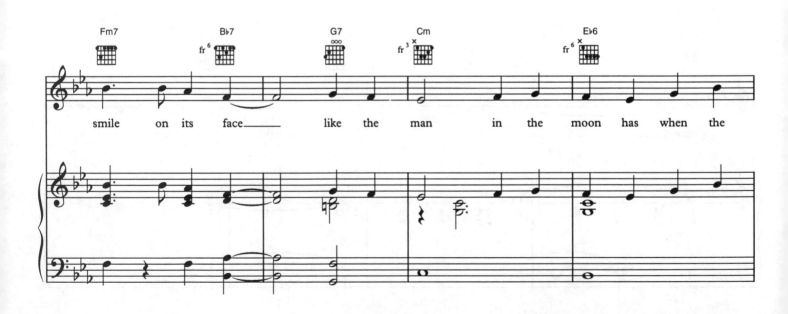

smile on its face____ like the man in the moon has when the

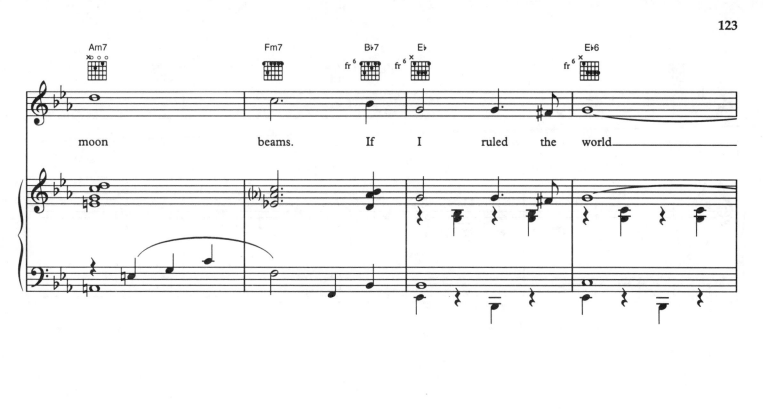

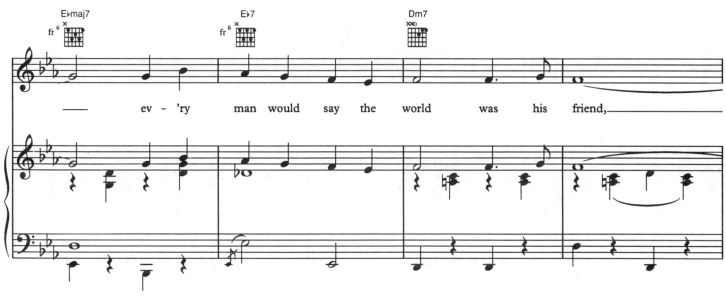

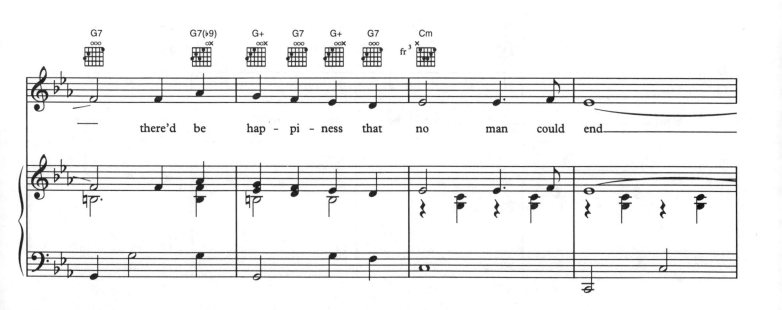

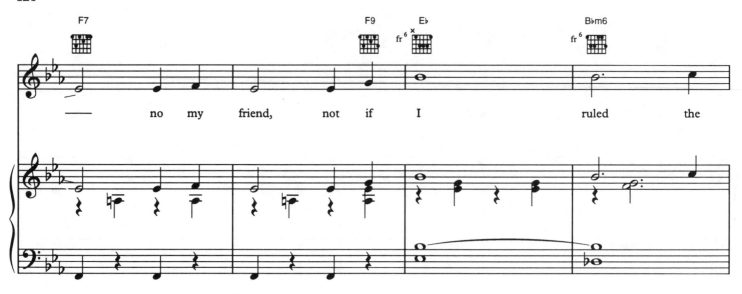

no my friend, not if I ruled the

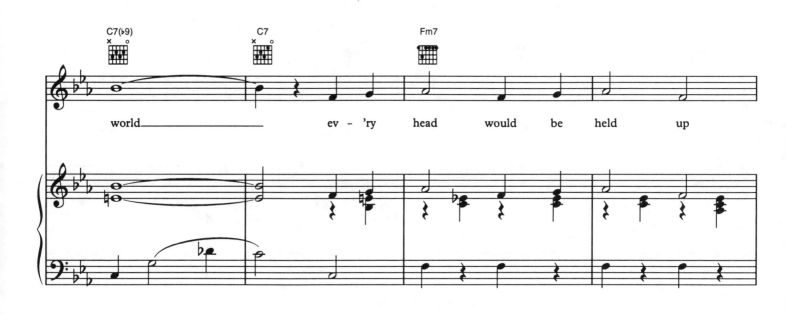

world _____ ev - 'ry head would be held up

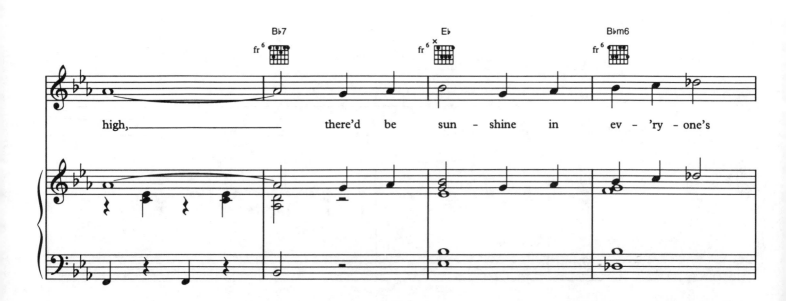

high, _____ there'd be sun - shine in ev - 'ry - one's

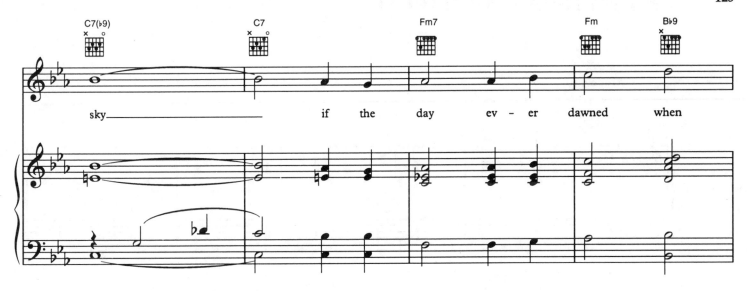

sky_____ if the day ev - er dawned when

I ruled the world._____

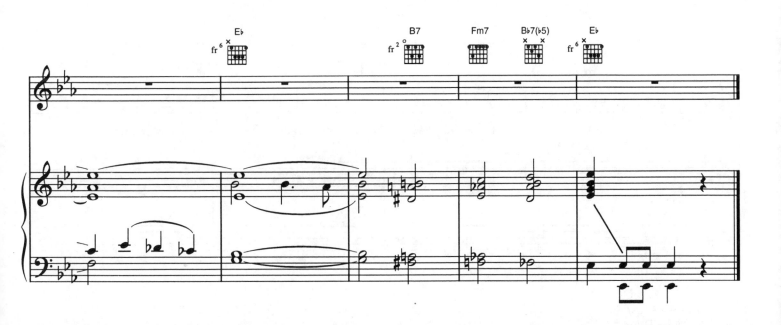

IF I WERE A CARPENTER

Words and Music by TIM HARDIN

127

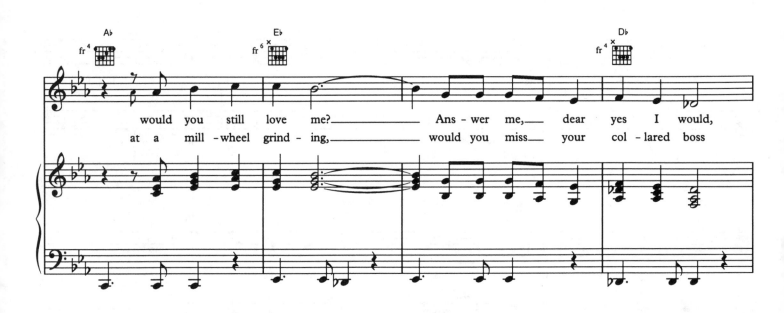

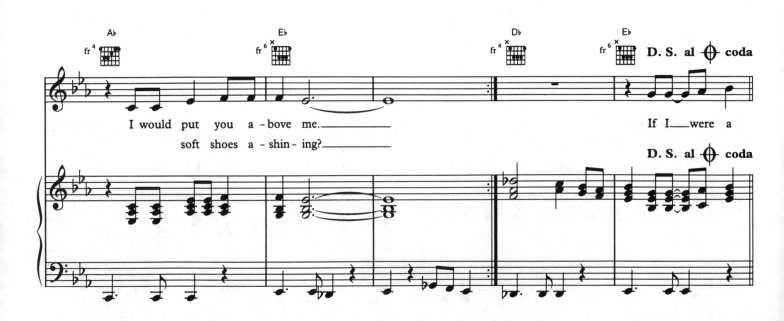

Coda

Would you mar – ry me an – y – way?_____

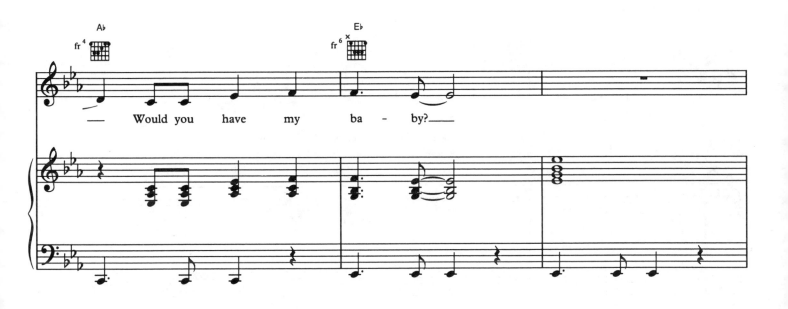

— Would you have my ba – by?_____

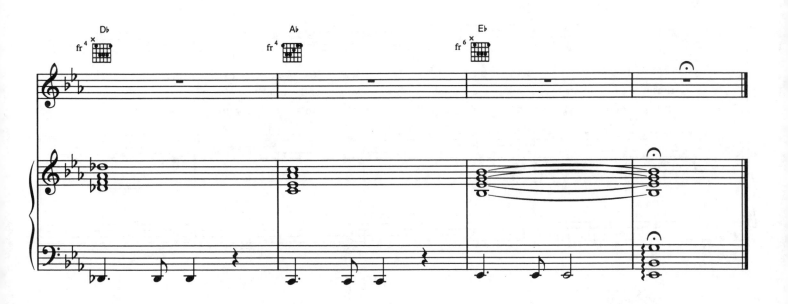

IT MIGHT AS WELL RAIN UNTIL SEPTEMBER

Words and Music by GERRY GOFFIN and CAROLE KING

Rubato

What should I write? What can I say How can I tell you how much I miss you?

Moderately, in rhythm

The wea-ther here has been as nice as it can be,
I don't need sun-ny skies for things I have to do,
It does-n't mat-ter wheth-er skies are grey or blue;

al-though it does-n't real-ly mat-ter much to me.
'cause I stay home the whole day long and think of you.
It's rain-ing in my heart 'cause I can't be with you.

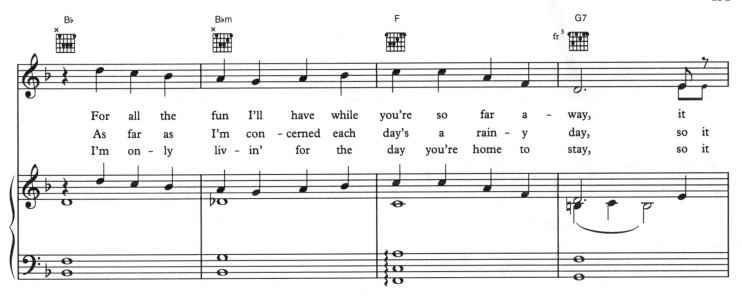

For all the fun I'll have while you're so far a - way, it
As far as I'm con - cerned each day's a rain - y day, so it
I'm on - ly liv - in' for the day you're home to stay, so it

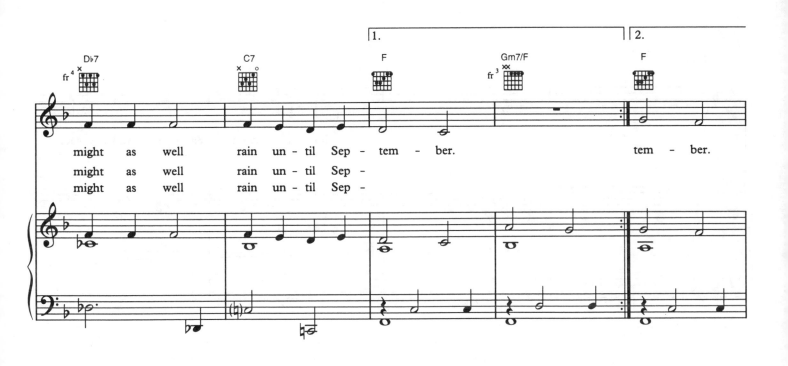

might as well rain un - til Sep - tem - ber. tem - ber.
might as well rain un - til Sep -
might as well rain un - til Sep -

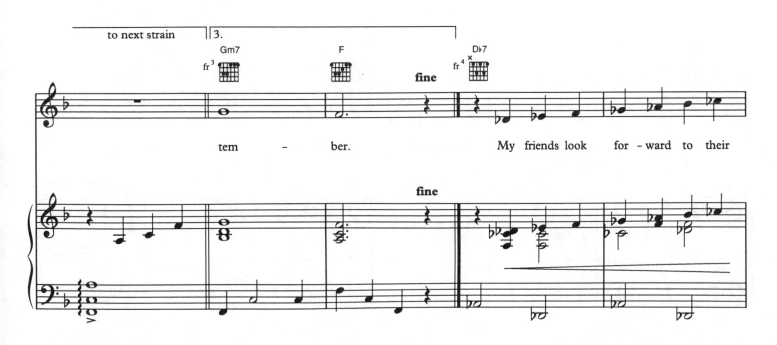

tem - ber. My friends look for - ward to their

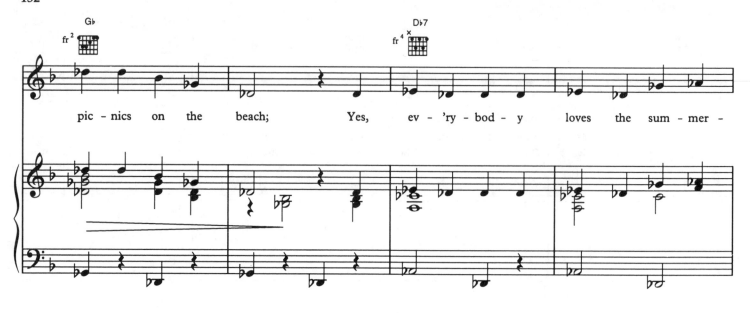

pic - nics on the beach; Yes, ev - 'ry - bod - y loves the sum - mer -

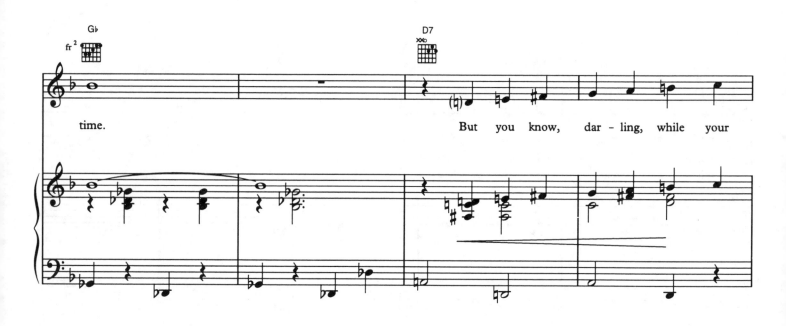

time. But you know, dar - ling, while your

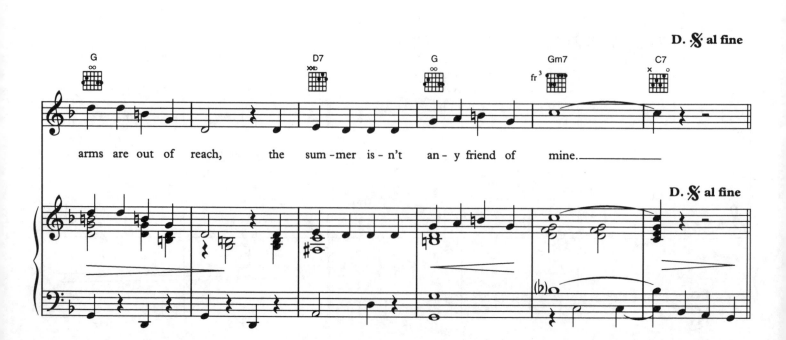

arms are out of reach, the sum - mer is - n't an - y friend of mine._____

D. %· al fine

IT MUST BE HIM

English Words by MACK DAVID
Original French Words by MAURICE VIDALIN
Music by GILBERT BECAUD

1. I tell my-self what's done is done, I tell my-self don't be a fool,
2. Af-ter a while, I'm my-self a-gain, I pick the pie-ces off the floor,

play the field, have a lot of fun, it's ea-sy when you play it cool.
put my heart on the shelf a-gain, he'll ne-ver hurt me a-ny-more.

I tell my-self, 'Don't be a chump, who cares? Let him stay a-way.'
I'm not a pup-pet on a string, I'll find some-bo-dy else some day,

134

JUST LOVING YOU

Words and Music by TOM SPRINGFIELD

LES BICYCLETTES DE BELSIZE

Words and Music by LES REED and BARRY MASON

LAST WALTZ

Words and Music by LES REED and BARRY MASON

Waltz moderato

I won - dered should I go or should I stay,____
Thought the love we had was go - in' strong,____

the band had on - ly one more song to play,____ and
through the good the bad we'd get a - long,____ and

144

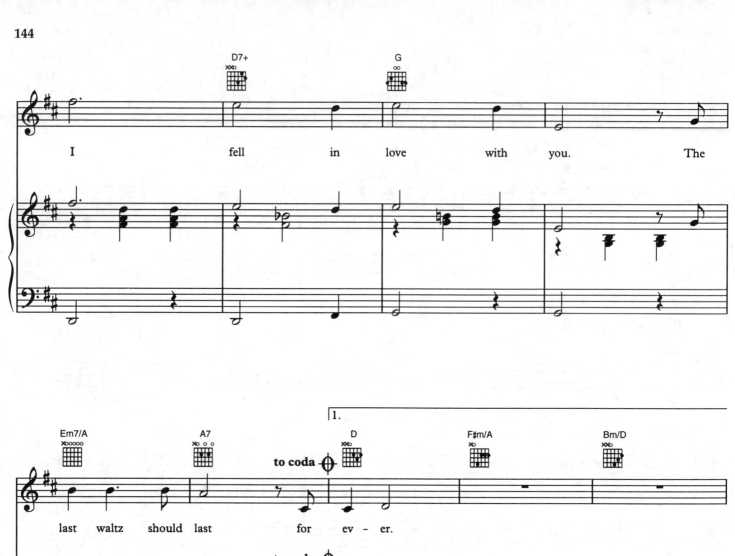

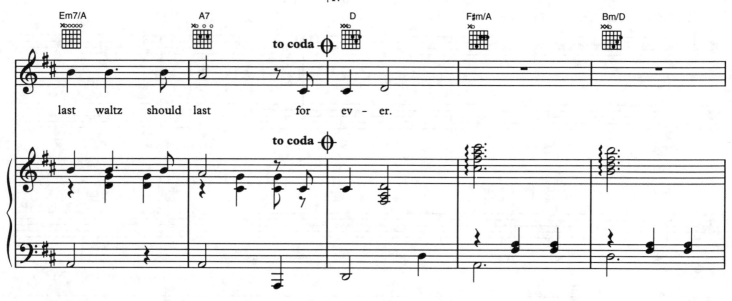

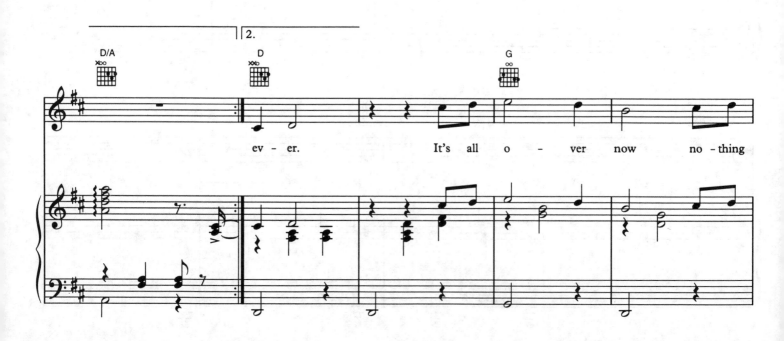

LITTLE CHILDREN

Words and Music by MORT SHUMAN and JOHN LESLIE McFARLAND

Lyrics:

1. Lit - tle child - ren,_ you'd bet - ter not tell on me,
(2.) - way, lit - tle child - ren,_ now why aren't you play - in' out - side?

I'm tell - in' you.__ Lit - tle child - ren,_
I'm ask - in' you.__ You can't fool me,_

you'd bet - ter not tell what you see,
'cause I'm gon - na know if you hide,

and if you're good,
and try to peep.

LITTLE GREEN APPLES

Words and Music by BOBBY RUSSELL

And she reach-es out an' takes my hand squeez-es it says: "how you feel-in'

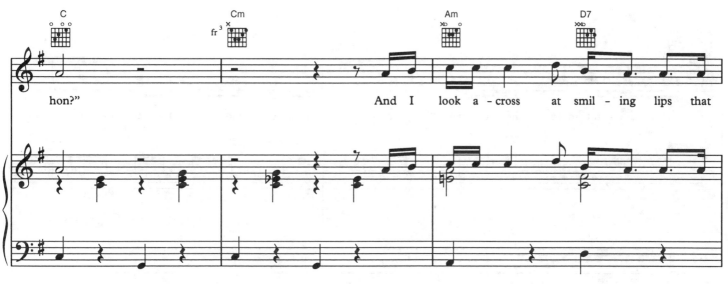

hon?" And I look a-cross at smil-ing lips that

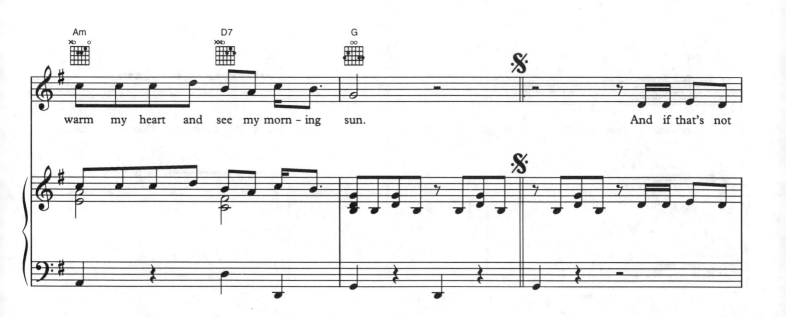

warm my heart and see my morn-ing sun. And if that's not

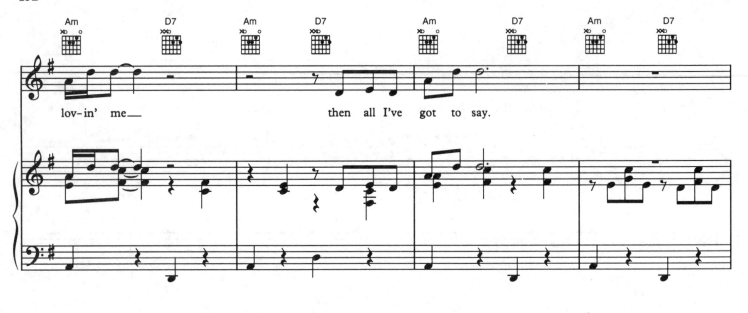

lov-in' me___ then all I've got to say.

God did-n't make lit-tle green ap-ples and it don't rain in In-di-an-ap-o-lis

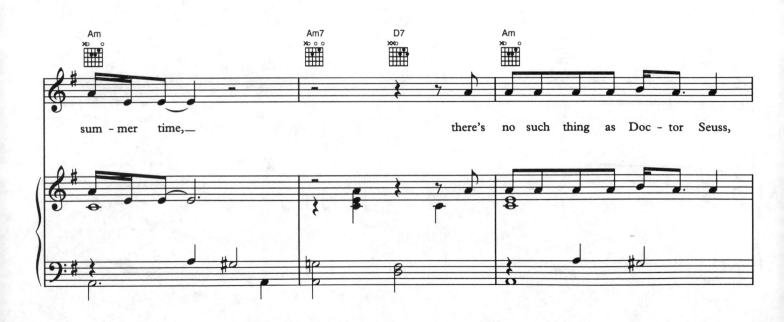

sum-mer time,___ there's no such thing as Doc-tor Seuss,

bite to eat __ and she drops what she's do-in' and

hur-ries down __ to meet me and I'm al-ways late. __ But

she sits wait-ing pa-tient-ly and smiles when she first sees me 'cause she's made that way.

D. 𝄋 al fine

THE LOCO-MOTION

Words and Music by GERRY GOFFIN and CAROLE KING

MY CHERIE AMOUR

Words and Music by STEVIE WONDER,
HENRY COSBY and SYLVIA MOY

MASSACHUSETTS

Words and Music by BARRY, ROBIN and MAURICE GIBB

Feel I'm go - ing back____ to Mas - sa - chu - setts;
Tried to hitch a ride____ to San Fran - cis - co;
Talk a - bout the life____ in Mas - sa - chu - setts;

some - thing's tell - ing me____ I must go home.____ And the
got - ta do the things____ I wan - na do.____ And the
speak a - bout the peo - ple I have seen.____ And the

MAY EACH DAY

Words by MORT GREEN
Music by GEORGE WYLE

Waltz Tempo

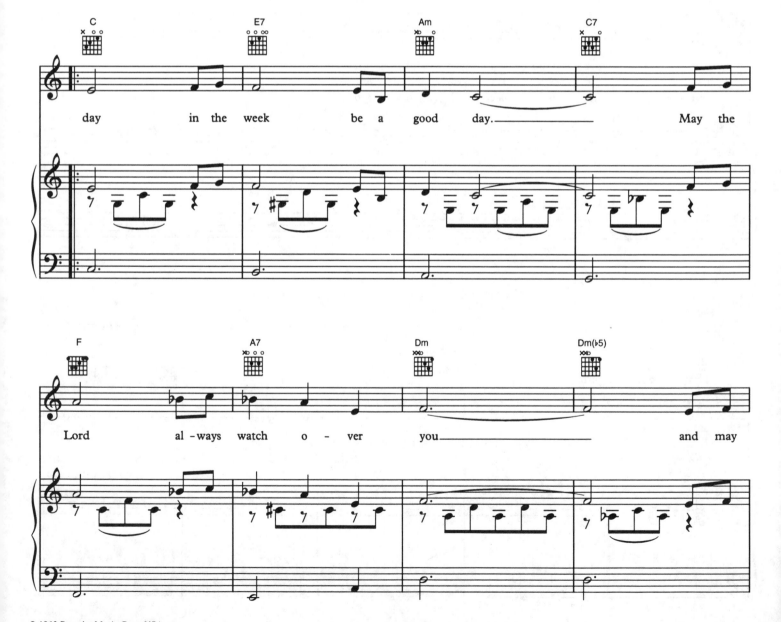

May each day in the week be a good day._____ May the

Lord al-ways watch o-ver you_____ and may

166

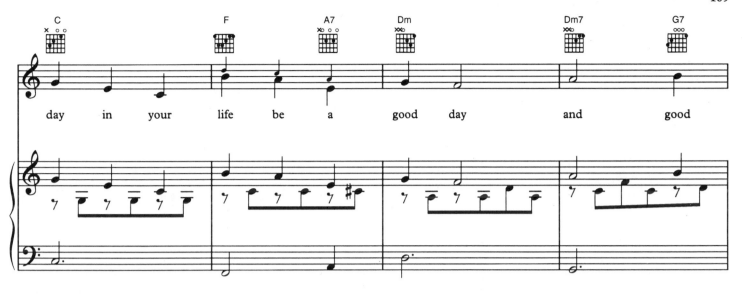

day in your life be a good day and good

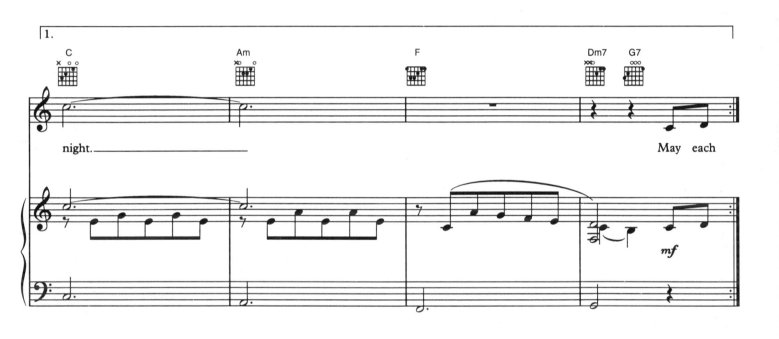

night._____

May each

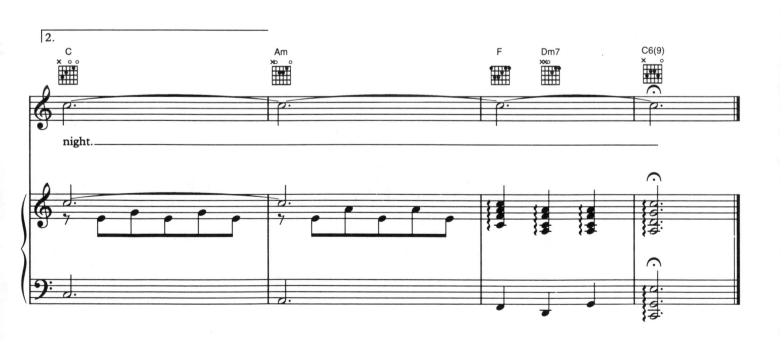

night._____

MILORD

Original Words by G MOUSTAKI,
English Words by BUNNY LEWIS
Music by MARGUERITE MONNOT

172

MY KIND OF GIRL

Words and Music by LESLIE BRICUSSE

MY WAY

Original Words by GILLES THIBAUT
English Words by PAUL ANKA
Music by CLAUDE FRANCOIS and JACQUES REVAUX

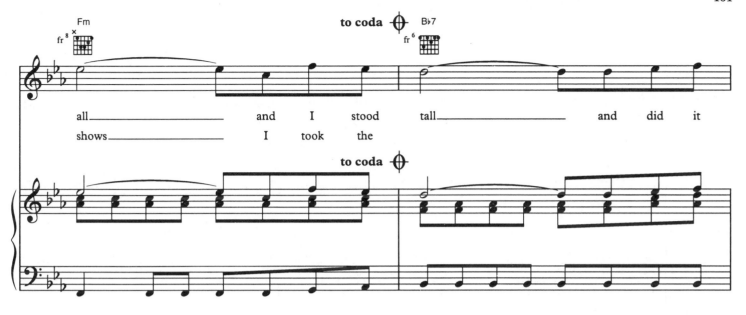

all_____ and I stood tall_____ and did it

shows_____ I took the

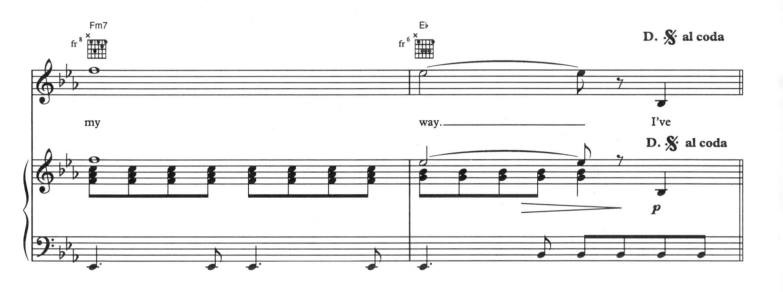

my way._____ I've

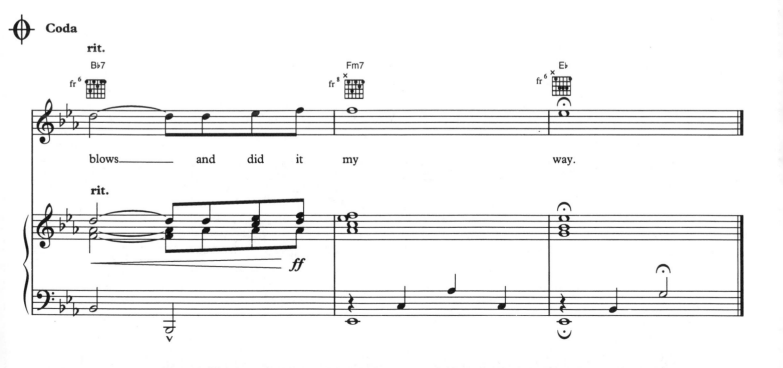

blows_____ and did it my way.

ON A CLEAR DAY (YOU CAN SEE FOREVER)

Words by ALAN JAY LERNER
Music by BURTON LANE

clear day_____ how it will as - tound you_____ that the

glow of your be - ing out - shines ev - 'ry star. You feel

part of_____ ev - 'ry moun - tain, sea and shore._____ You can

184

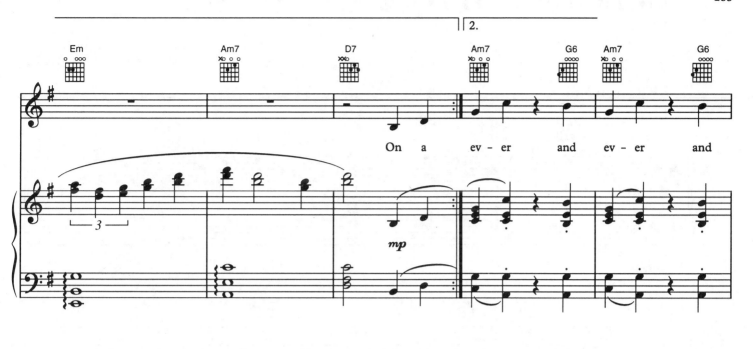

On a ev - er and ev - er and

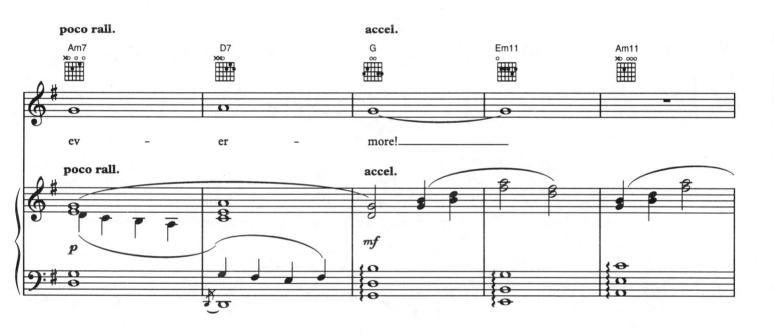

ev - er - more!

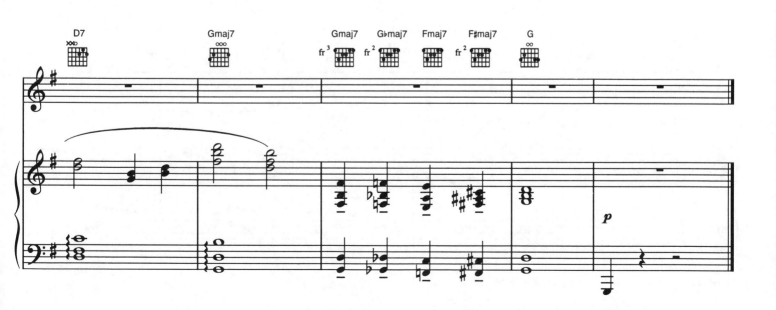

PORTRAIT OF MY LOVE

Words by DAVID WEST
Music by CYRIL ORNADEL

PUPPET ON A STRING

Words by PHIL COULTER
Music by BILL MARTIN

Moderato (alla Calliope)

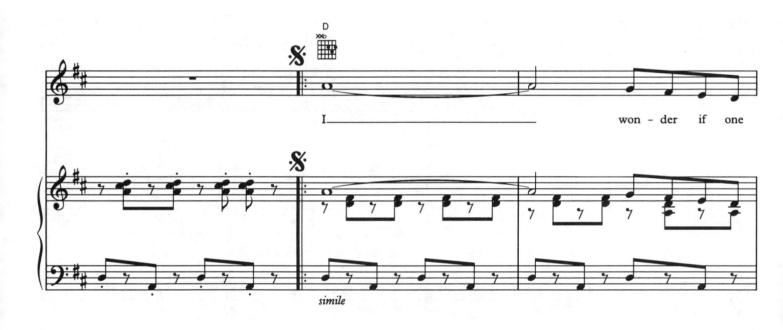

there, like a pup-pet on a string!_____

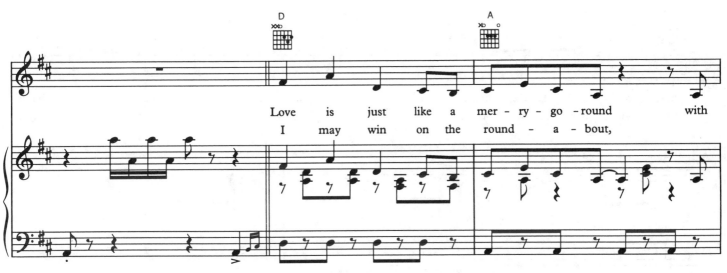

Love is just like a mer-ry-go-round with
I may win on the round-a-bout,

all the fun of the fair.____ One day I'm feel-ing
then I lose on the swings____ In or out, there is

down on the ground   then I'm up in the air.____
nev - er a doubt   just who's pull - ing the strings.____

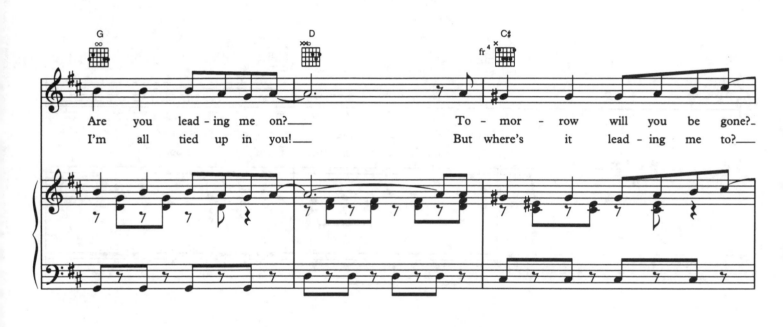

Are you lead - ing me on?____   To - mor - row will you be gone?____
I'm all tied up in you!____   But where's it lead - ing me to?____

D.S. al ⊕ coda

D.S. al ⊕ coda

I_____ won-der if one day that you'll say that you care, if you say you love me mad - ly, I'd glad - ly be there, like a pup-pet on a string!_____

Like a pup-pet on a string!

SAY WONDERFUL THINGS

Words and Music by NORMAN NEWELL and PHIL GREEN

194

SOFTLY, AS I LEAVE YOU

Original Words by G CALABRESE
English Words by HAL SHAPER
Music by ANTONIO DE VITA

SILENCE IS GOLDEN

Words and Music by BOB CREWE and BOB GAUDIO

SPANISH EYES (MOON OVER NAPLES)

Words by CHARLES SINGLETON and EDDIE SNYDER
Music by BERT KAEMPFERT

1. Blue Span-ish eyes, tear-drops are fall-ing from your Span-ish eyes. Please, please don't cry, this is just a-dios and not good-bye. Soon

2. Blue Span-ish eyes, pret-ti-est eyes in all of Mex-i-co. True Span-ish eyes, please smile for me once more be-fore I go.

STRANGER ON THE SHORE

Words by ROBERT MELLIN
Music by ACKER BILK

Moderato (with feeling)

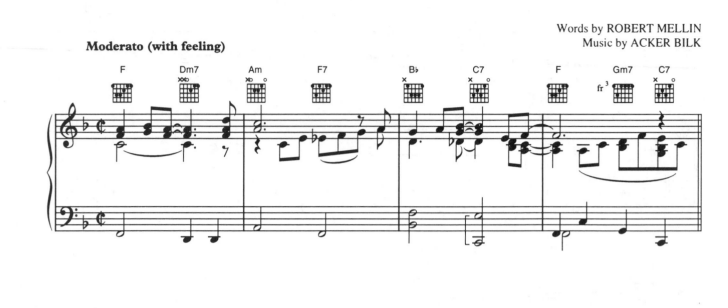

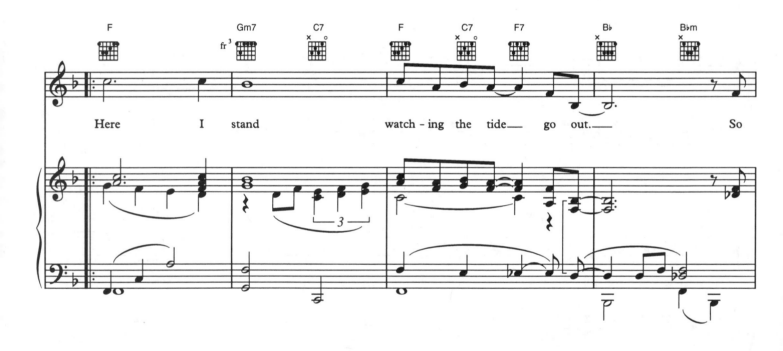

Here I stand watch-ing the tide go out. So

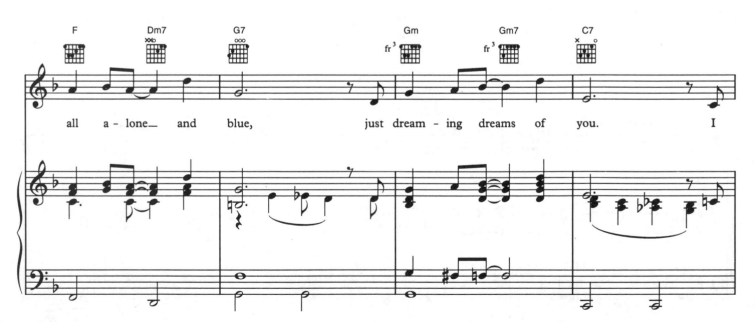

all a-lone and blue, just dream-ing dreams of you. I

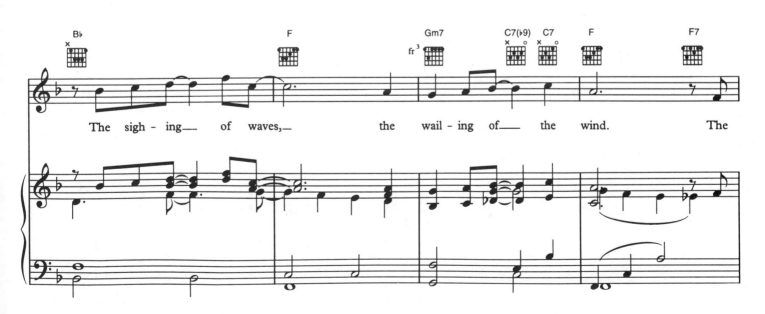

tears in my eyes burn___ plead - ing "My love,___ re - turn."___

Why oh why must I go on___ like this?___ Shall I just be___ a

lone - ly strang - er on___ the shore?___

TAKE THESE CHAINS FROM MY HEART

Words and Music by FRED ROSE and HY HEATH

Take these chains from my heart and set me free. _____ You've grown
heart just a word of sym-pa-thy. _____ Be as

cold and no lon-ger care for me. _____ All my
fair to my heart as you can be. _____ Then if

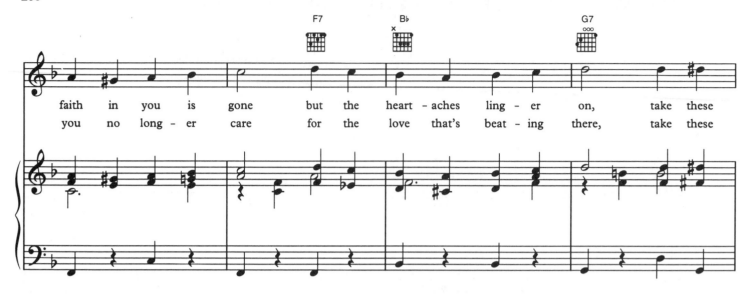

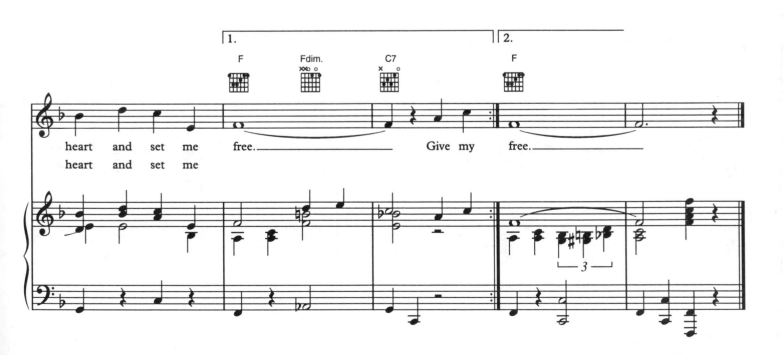

THERE GOES MY EVERYTHING

Words and Music by DALLAS FRAZIER

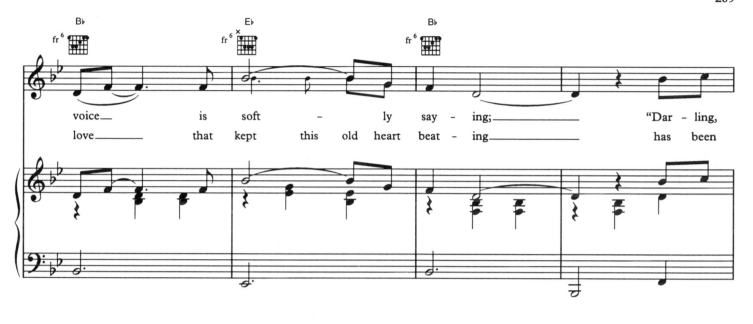

voice___ is soft - ly say - ing;_____ "Dar - ling,
love___ that kept this old heart beat - ing_____ has been

this will be good - bye___ for - ev - er - more."_____
shat - tered by the clos - ing of the door.___

There goes my rea - son for liv - ing,

there goes the one of my dreams,_____ there goes my

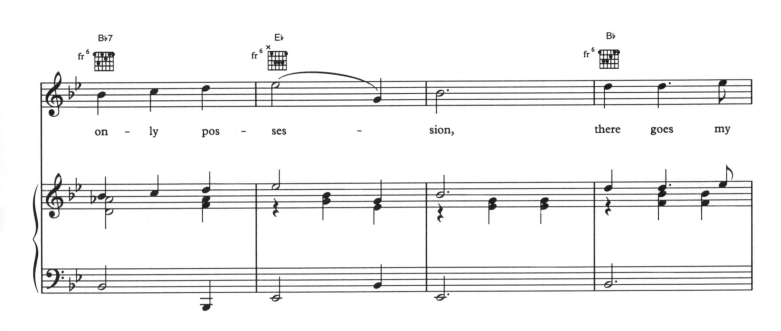

on - ly pos - ses - sion, there goes my

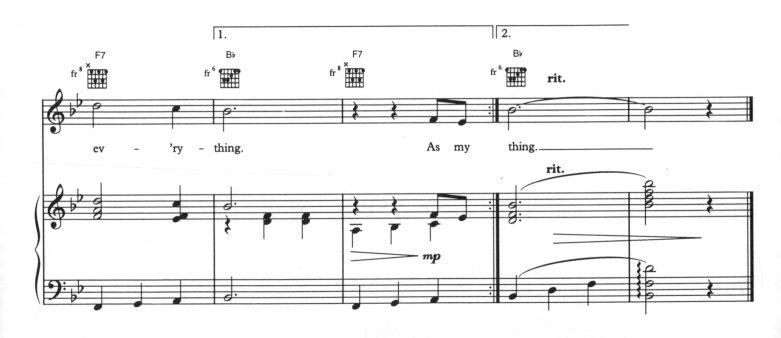

ev - 'ry - thing. As my thing._____

THERE'S A KIND OF HUSH (ALL OVER THE WORLD)

Words and Music by
LES REED and GEOFF STEPHENS

TRY TO REMEMBER

Words by TOM JONES
Music by HARVEY SCHMIDT

216

UP ON THE ROOF

Words and Music by GERRY GOFFIN and CAROLE KING

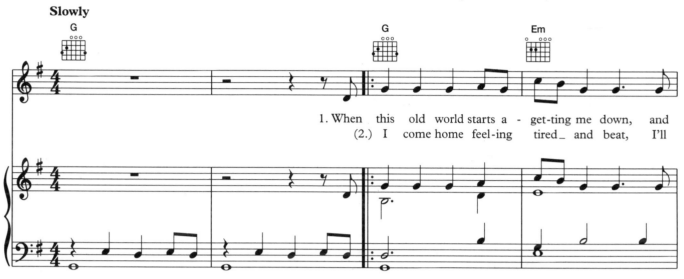

1. When this old world starts a - get-ting me down, and
(2.) I come home feel-ing tired and beat, I'll

peo - ple are just too much for me to face, I'll
go up where the air is fresh and sweet, I'll

climb 'way up to the top of the stairs, and all my cares just drift right in - to
get far a - way from the hust - ling crowd, and all that rat - race noise down in the

UP-UP AND AWAY

Words and Music by JIM WEBB

Brightly

Would you like___ to ride___ in my___ beau - ti - ful___ bal - loon?
world's a ni - cer place___ in my___ beau - ti - ful___ bal - loon,
Love is wait - ing there___ in my___ beau - ti - ful___ bal - loon,

Would you like___ to glide___ in my___ beau - ti - ful___ bal - loon?
it wears a ni - cer face___ in my___ beau - ti - ful___ bal - loon.
way up in___ the air___ in my___ beau - ti - ful___ bal - loon.

WALK AWAY

English Words by DON BLACK
Music by UDO JURGENS

© 1964 Edition Montana, Germany
Ardmore & Beechwood Ltd, London WC2H 0EA

THE WEDDING

English Lyrics by FRED JAY
Original Words and Music by JOAQUIN PRIETO

229

Verse: true - oo. I___ see the church, I see the peo - ple, your___ folks and mine hap - py and smil - ing, and___ I can hear sweet voi - ces sing - ing, "A - ve Ma - ri - a." Oh my love,___ my love___ this can real - ly be___ that some day___ you'll walk___ down the

aisle____ with me,____ let it be,____ make it be that I'm the one____ for you,____ I'd be

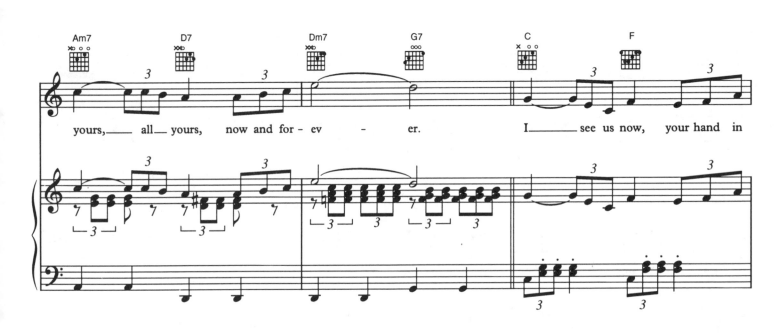

yours,____ all__ yours, now and for - ev - er. I____ see us now, your hand in

my hand, this____ is the hour, this is the mo - ment,

WHAT A WONDERFUL WORLD

Words and Music by GEORGE DAVID WEISS and BOB THIELE

233

WINCHESTER CATHEDRAL

Words and Music by GEOFF STEPHENS

THE WHITE ROSE OF ATHENS

Words by NORMAN NEWALL
Additional Words by ARCHIE BLEYER
Music by MANOS HADJIDAKIS

1. The sum-mer days are end - ing in the val - ley, _____ and now the
2. The au-tumn leaves are fall - ing in the val - ley, _____ and soon the

time has come when we must be a - part, _____ but like the rose, that comes back with the
win - ter snow will lie up - on the ground, _____ but then I know, I know that like the

spring - time, _____ you will re - turn to bring the sum - mer to my heart. _____
ros - es, _____ you will come back a - gain when spring-time comes a - round. _____

A WHITER SHADE OF PALE

Words and Music by KEITH REID and GARY BROOKER

1. We skipped the light fan - dan-go, and turned cart-wheels 'cross the floor,
2. She said, 'There is no rea-son, and the truth is____ plain to see',

I was feel - ing kind of sea-sick, but the crowd called out for more.
but I wan-dered through my play-ing cards, and would not_ let her be.

WORDS

Words and Music by BARRY, ROBIN and MAURICE GIBB

Smile an ev-er-last-ing smile, a smile could bring you near to me.___

___ Don't ev-er let me find you gone 'cause that would bring a

244

A WORLD OF OUR OWN

Words and Music by TOM SPRINGFIELD

YOU DON'T HAVE TO SAY YOU LOVE ME

Original Italian Words by V PALLAVICINI
English Lyrics by VICKI WICKHAM and SIMON NAPIER-BELL
Music by P DONAGGIO

way.   Don't you see that now_____ you've gone,_____

— and I'm left here on my own_____ that I have to

fol - low you   and beg   you to   come   home.

YOU'RE MY WORLD (IL MIO MONDO)

Original Words by GINO PAOLI
English Words by CARL SIGMAN
Music by UMBERTO BINDI

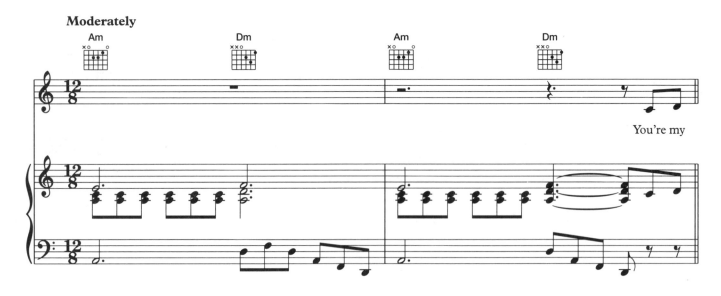

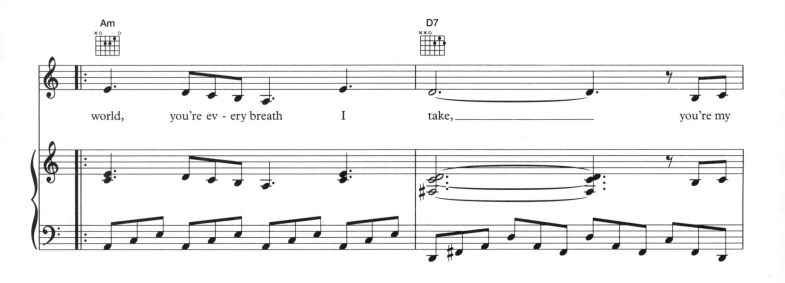

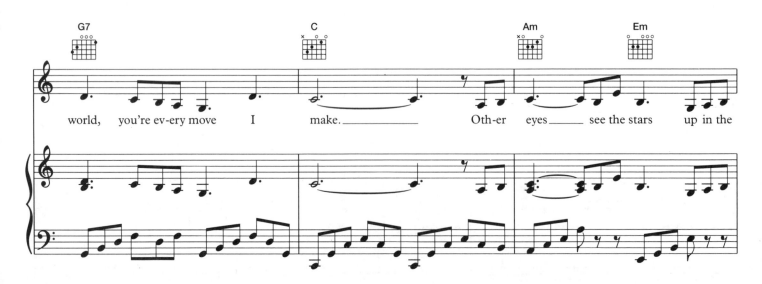

258

Printed in England

100 YEARS OF POPULAR MUSIC

Vol. 1 - 9817A

9816A

Vol. 1 - 9819A

Vol. 1 - 9821A

Vol. 2 - 9818A

Vol. 1 - 9823A

Vol. 2 - 9820A

Vol. 2 - 9822A

Vol. 2 - 9824A

IMP's Exciting New Series!

100 YEARS OF POPULAR MUSIC

Vol. 1 - 9825A

Vol. 1 - 9827A

Vol. 1 - 9829A

Vol. 1 - 9831A

Vol. 2 - 9826A

Vol. 2 - 9828A

Vol. 2 - 9830A

Vol. 2 - 9832A

Vol. 2 - 9833A

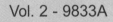

IMP
International
MUSIC
Publications

IMP's Exciting New Series!